Vocab

skills

WILLIAM EDMONDS

TEACHER TIMESAVERS

Published by Scholastic Ltd,
Villiers House,
Clarendon Avenue,
Leamington Spa,
Warwickshire CV32 5PR

Author William Edmonds
Editor Irene Goodacre
Assistant editor Joanne Boden
Series designer Joy White
Designers Micky Pledge and Sue Stockbridge
Illustrations Liz Thomas
Cover illustration Frances Lloyd
Cover photograph Martyn Chillmaid

Designed using Aldus Pagemaker
Printed in Great Britain by Clays Ltd, Bungay, Suffolk

British Library Cataloguing-in-Publication Data
A catalogue record for this book is
available from the British Library.

ISBN 0-590-533452

Contents

Teacher's notes 5
Feature grid 13
Topic grid 14

Vocabulary recognition
A train journey 15
A story train 16
Classroom labels 17
Wild animals! 18
Fruit and vegetable labels 19
Toy shop labels 20
A shopping game 21
Shopping game: 2 22
Going on holiday 23
Pairing 24
Pairing and ordering 25
Opposite sides – opposite words 26
Deciding on days 27
Calendar months 28

Vocabulary construction
Ten hens 29
Sound-and-look-alike words 30
Rhyme time 31
A car word-maker 32
Sunny words 33
Label the pictures: 1 34
Label the pictures: 2 35
Label the pictures: 3 36
My favourite -ing words 37
What am I doing all day? 38
In and out 39
Over and under 40
Discovering 41
Doing and undoing 42
Making use of prefixes 43
Pre-fixing 44
Around port 45
Information 46
Preparations 47
Constructions 48
An unbeatable gift 49
Become a tryer, thinker, writer... 50
What am I full of? 51
Reasonableness – about yourself 52
Going into the past 53
Kate's big ed-venture 54
Sensationalism 55
Simple simplification 56

Vocabulary at work
Household nouns 57
Nouns we love best 58
A roll-call of names 59
The noun family 60
Naming my favourite nouns 61
Monster adjectives 62
Funny faces 63
Amazing zany things 64
My favourite adjectives 65
What did the cat do with the mouse? 66
What do they do? 67
My favourite verbs 68
Which way is it? 69
Using adverbs advisedly 70
Tremendously revealing comments 71
Investigating articles 72
Investigating more articles 73
Join in with conjunctions 74
Finding personal pronouns 75
What is it? 76

Vocabulary research
Make a zigzag abc picture strip: 1 77
Make a zigzag abc picture strip: 2 78
A dictionary questionnaire 79
An unusual folding abc 80
The a-team 81
A galaxy of g- words 82
A shower of sh- words 83

A q- quiz 84
A pick of p- creatures 85
A c- feast 86
Sorting out your relations 87
What does a thesaurus offer? 88
Good and bad 89
In other words 90
From start to finish 91
Extra special words 92
An abc of similarities 93
A folding abc of opposites 94
What's the difference? 95
One letter out – what's the difference? 96
Same words – four different meanings! 97
The gist of a story 98
A part-of-speech survey 99
A word popularity survey 100

Vocabulary selection

Greetings! 101
Writing a thank-you letter 102
A request letter 103
Questions of spelling: 1 104
Questions of spelling: 2 105
Questions of odd spelling 106
What odd 'weirds'! 107
Which 'weird' is it? 108
Odd 'weirds' out! 109
Monkey's ... adventure 110
A 'great' story 111
Instead of 'said' 112
Going on and on and on 113
Is it 'it's' or 'its'? 114

Expressive vocabulary

My mum 115
My lovely pet 116
My friend 117
On cloud nine 118
Feeling sad 119
It was a dark, dark night 120
Fire! Fire! 121
Wet through 122
Like a volcano 123
Like a beautiful bird 124
Christmas is coming! 125
On a cold and frosty morning 126
Sing a song of summer days 127
Yes to/No to 128

Specialist vocabulary

What about me? 129
Shapes galore 130
What shapes make up these towers? 131
Us (and our neighbours) in space 132
Times 133
Flowers, fruits and vegetables 134
Introduce yourself to insects 135
A zigzag selection of animals 136
A zigzag collection of places 137
The top ten words 138

Vocabulary round-up

My favourite word 139
Amazing words 140
Crazy words 141
New word banking 142
Bank book 143
See my skills with words 144

Teachers' Notes

About the author

William Edmonds is a former primary school teacher, now working full-time as a writer.

Why vocabulary skills?

Words are riches – they are probably the greatest of all the treasures that we possess. Just imagine living in a world without them: no talk, nothing to read and write; no way of making good friends; nothing to argue with, agree, plan, remember, develop understanding or just banter with; no stories, no questions, no answers, no requests, no information, no songs, no chatter, no gossip!

More than that, words are magic. They are magical symbols – odd sounds or squiggles – that enable us to represent, think about and share our experiences of the world around us. They fire our imaginations, bring excitement and sensitivity; they make anything seem possible. They therefore have immense power to shape the way we live.

Naturally we need to savour and exploit these magical riches as much as we can. For all of us, the acquisition of an extensive vocabulary, with the ability to use it adeptly in every kind of context, should be a top priority. Getting to know the right words is, after all, the cornerstone of all learning. When we have plenty of choice words at our disposal then we also have a good all-round knowledge and a strong capacity for communicating, and for understanding the world around us.

Vocabulary learning is given strong emphasis in all sections of English programmes of study of the UK National Curricula. The English programmes specifically refer to 'pupils' knowledge of vocabulary... developed through reading' and to children being taught to 'consider carefully the words they use'. Particular importance is attached to 'the use of widening vocabulary' and the appreciation of 'apt' and 'appropriate' words.

At the same time it should be appreciated that our current standard English is a *live* language which quite naturally is evolving all the time. Much of it was once 'non-standard'. Shakespeare introduced a large number of new (then non-standard) words into the English language, they became standard English and, of course, many of them have now ceased to be so. Sensitivity to the vibrancy of our language in this regard is therefore very important and may be a little overlooked in the current official policy.

What vocabulary skills?

This book contains 130 photocopiable sheets designed to help children practise and develop vocabulary skills. These are grouped in eight broad sections as follows:

- Vocabulary recognition – developing early reading skills.
- Vocabulary construction – building words from different word parts.
- Vocabulary at work – words playing grammatical roles.
- Vocabulary research – using a dictionary and a thesaurus.
- Vocabulary selection – choosing appropriate words and spellings.
- Expressive vocabulary – using words which appeal to the individual.
- Specialist vocabulary – learning terms relevant to specific subject areas.
- Vocabulary round-up – collecting words together.

The sheets are graded in order of difficulty with work appropriate to Key Stage 1 placed at the beginning of each section. Through the book, the sections become more sophisticated and analytical in approach and, while some sections concentrate on particular skills, those skills may also be dealt with elsewhere, allowing children to practise and reinforce their learning. Two grids at the end of these notes (pages 13 and 14) indicate where particular features and topics are met in the book.

How? Making best use of each page

School desks or drawers can easily fill up with half-worked and scuffed loose photocopiable sheets. This book aims to avoid this problem by suggesting a variety of ways to make full use of the pages.

- Papers to cut out, fold and work:

Pupils are asked to cut out and fold pages in a number of activities. A dashed line like - - - - - should be cut out, a dotted line like ...... should be folded. On pages 15 and 16 these procedures are used to make stand-up words that can be put together to form 'trains' which spell out a range of sentences.

Other pages involve making stand-up figures and labels. Some activities in the Expressive Vocabulary section involve cutting out a shape, working on it and then hanging it up.

• Papers to be gathered into a folder book:
Most of the activities are presented in the long horizontal or 'landscape' form. Why not ask the children to make their own card folders or covers for these? The pages can then be collated and held together with strong paper clips. Pupils could even make their own covers and contents lists (see pages 143 and 144). By doing this, children can take real pride in their work and see that it is genuinely building up as they acquire a good range of skills.

• Papers to be folded into small booklets or brochures:
Some of the activities involve folding the sheets in half (or sometimes thirds and quarters) to make brochures or booklets. When this occurs the children are meant to fill in both sides of the sheet.

On some of the pages (for example pages 61 and 141) the outside part is printed on and directions are given to help children complete both sides. A dotted central dividing line shows where the paper can be folded to put the main work inside a four-page booklet.

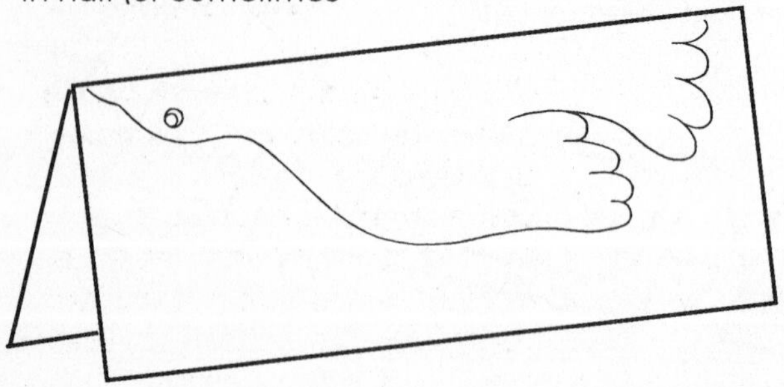

• Pages for display:
Some of the pages, especially in the Expressive and Specialist Vocabulary sections, lend themselves to individual creative work with colours or further illustrations so that they can then be displayed on classroom or school display boards. Teachers and children should also bear in mind that the all-round outside margins of the papers can be suitably decorated and coloured as frames for display sheets.

A guide to the worksheets in each section

Activities include clear instructions, but in most cases it will still help if a little discussion and explanation takes place before the children start work. The following run-down of contents gives an idea of what each activity is about, and how it can be approached.

Vocabulary recognition

This first section introduces a variety of ways in which children can learn to recognise the written word.

A train journey and **A story train** ask pupils to make model trains from word engines and carriages of small folded papers that can be arranged in different combinations and orders (for example, 'We are going shopping' or 'Once there were ten terrible bears'). These are constructed by cutting on the - - - - lines and folding on the ..... lines. (With young children some prior guillotining along the - - - - lines may help to speed up the process.) Children may write their own names, and those of friends, on the three blank carriages on the first sheet.

Classroom labels provides folding stand-up labels which can be placed (or stuck with Blu-Tack) around the classroom. The labels could first be coloured with a felt-tipped pen or crayon.

Wild animals! contains outlines of stand-up figures and labels to go with them. The labels can also be used as mini flash-cards for testing games.

Fruit and vegetable labels and **Toy shop labels** also provide labels to be cut out and placed appropriately.

A shopping game consists of two sheets that need to be cut up (the teacher could guillotine these in advance) so that groups of four children (plus one 'shopkeeper') can play a simple game. They should take it in turns to 'buy' items of shopping, using the named pictures on the shopping item tickets to help them identify all the words on their lists. The game should *not* become competitive!

Going on holiday asks children to write a packing list on the side of a suitcase. A collection of possible items is given on the right-hand side of the page. Children should look at these carefully, but fold the pictures under before filling in their list.

Pairing and **Pairing and ordering** both provide material for word-to-word matching exercises. The first requires children to distinguish small differences between words which are similar in appearance, the second asks them to order written numbers.

Opposite sides – opposite words leads to the making of simple stand-up folded word cards where antonyms should be found and written on the blank sides. Once this is done the compilers can quiz other children on what might be hidden from view on the reverse sides. (Light/dark and light/heavy could trick some unsuspecting players.)

Deciding on days asks children to choose correct spellings for the days of the week and then to complete two open diary pages. As an extension of this activity children could be asked to choose their favourite day of the week and write about, or draw a picture of, something they do on that day.

Calendar months concludes this section and asks for the names of the months to be rewritten, in order, on a basic calendar.

Vocabulary construction

This is a major section which looks into the range of components or particular letter arrangements that go into the making of words. It starts by raising the children's awareness of common beginnings, middles and ends of words and then goes on to demonstrate how vocabulary can be built up and extended by adding prefixes and suffixes.

Ten hens asks children to compose, with the help of first letter clues, words with an -en or -end ending. One word should be written on each of the pictured ten hens, any other words children think of can be written on the other side of the page.

Sound-and-look-alike words invites children to write -ell words on a bell, -and words on a hand, and -ake words on a cake.

Rhyme time introduces six more groups of sound-and-look-alike words, but for each group brings in one exception to the rule like school/tool/fool/**rule** and Ted/bed/red/**said**. The children could be asked to use dictionaries to check their 'odd spelling' examples.

A car word-maker involves the making of words beginning with car- by constructing a simple word maker which has a strip of word-endings passing through two slits in a pictured car.

Sunny words asks for eight words beginning with sun- which children should write in on the lines of its beams.

Label the pictures: 1, 2 and **3** each provide nine pictures which should be labelled with clues of word beginnings and endings that are listed down each side of the page. The complete words can either be written directly on to the label spaces or else the parts can be cut out, assembled and glued into place.

My favourite -ing words and **What am I doing all day?** both ask for words to be composed with the -ing suffix. The second sheet is more open-ended and children should be made aware of the various problems that can occur when adding -ing (words that drop a final -e or double their last letter).

In and out asks for words to be put together with the prefixes in- and out-.

Over and under looks for words beginning with the prefixes over- and under-.

Discovering looks at the prefix dis- to show that it sometimes, but not always, serves as an opposing prefix. As an extension activity children could be asked to find diss- words – these are relatively rare and the activity would require careful use of a dictionary.

Doing and undoing requires the making and examining of words with the un- prefix. As an extension, children could be asked to make a list of unpleasant un- words, such as uncomfortable, uncaring or unspeakable, on the other side of the page.

Making use of prefixes asks children to label a selection of items which begin with the prefixes: uni-, bi-, tri-, tele-, mini- and micro-.

Pre-fixing deals with making new words which have the prefixes pre-, re- and de- and asks pupils to distinguish the different meanings of some of them. Make sure that children know the prefixes cannot be joined to all the endings and encourage them to write out the meanings of other words they have found on the back of the page.

Around port, Information, Preparations and **Constructions** all involve constructing words with a variety of prefixes and/or suffixes around the word cores -port-, -form-, -par- and -fer-, -duct- and -struct-.

An unbeatable gift asks for words with the suffix -able to be put as labels on a surprise gift parcel.

Become a tryer, thinker, writer... shows how the suffix -er changes certain verbs into nouns and **What am I full of?** shows how certain nouns can become adjectives.

Reasonableness – about yourself tries to be reasonable about the use of the suffix -ness, showing how sometimes it is used to absurd excess. Extend this activity by asking children to make up a list of -ness words that can be improved – for example generosity instead of generousness.

Going into the past sees how the regular past tense works by adding -ed while **Kate's big ed-venture** challenges children to find correct irregular past tense verb forms in a story filled with misspellings.

Sensationalism is about extending simple words with multiple suffixes.

Simple simplification looks at words with the -ion suffix and asks pupils to identify their original root words.

Vocabulary at work

Here the principal parts of speech are introduced as words that work by fulfilling particular grammatical roles. The activities deal successively with nouns, adjectives, verbs, adverbs, articles, conjunctions and pronouns. With **Household nouns** and **Nouns we love best** children are asked to provide nouns for particular basic contexts. In **Household nouns** children could be encouraged to 'build' an extension by adding rooms or noun lists on the back of the page.

A roll-call of names provides an opportunity for making an alphabetical list of proper nouns, like a class register or a list of place names.

The noun family makes a kind of family tree asking pupils to list proper and common nouns in different sub-categories like concrete, abstract or collective nouns. This is a difficult activity as children may not easily grasp the concept of concrete/abstract nouns. The family of nouns could be extended over the page.

Naming my favourite nouns (and the later **My favourite adjectives** and **My favourite verbs**) requires folding the sheet in half to make a four-page booklet. Instructions and visual clues are given for front and back pages and briefly for the inside pages – the reverse side of the sheet. On the first inside page children are asked to write names of people, and on the second, names of places. These should be supported with illustrations.

Monster adjectives has a selection of adjectives around the edge of the page and asks children to choose adjectives for an imaginary monster which they then have to draw.

Funny faces has a selection of adjectives from which pupils can choose in order to label a row of different funny faces, before drawing and labelling more faces of their own.

Amazing zany things involves making an a to z of adjectives in pairs which can be used to describe all kinds of 'things'.

My favourite adjectives – another four-page booklet, asking for adjectives to describe different friends and relations on the first inside page (page 2) and for adjectives to describe 'My toys and pets' on page 3.

What did the cat do with the mouse? seeks past tense verbs as suggestions of possible actions by a cat or a mouse.

What do they do? asks for simple present tense verbs for common actions of various people,

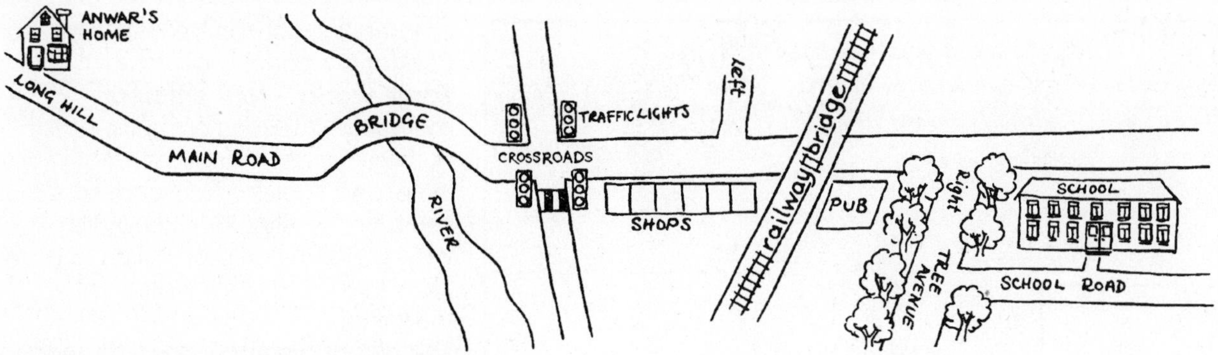

animals and inanimate objects. Children can extend this activity by writing 'What they don't do' on the back of the page.

My favourite verbs follows the form of the previous four-page booklets on nouns and adjectives and has space on the inside pages for children to write what they like doing when they are not at school. On page 2 they could perhaps list verbs associated with 'after school' and on page 3 verbs associated with 'weekends and holidays'.

Which way is it? asks children to think of and put down suitable directional prepositions to guide Anwar on his way to school as shown on a simple map. As an extension, ask pupils to write out their own directions home from school on the other side of the page.

Using adverbs advisedly involves selecting from a range of adverbs displayed around the page.

Tremendously revealing comments is an absolutely amazing way of stringing adverbs and adjectives together prompted by some given listed examples.

Investigating articles asks pupils some searching questions about the function of the articles 'a', 'an' and 'the'.

Investigating more articles carries the investigation further by looking at 'any' and 'some' and asks children to make an 'article ratings' survey. As an extension, ask pupils to investigate masculine and feminine articles in other European languages.

Join in with conjunctions – 'Look carefully and/or/when/if/although/unless/ because/but/until...': using assorted conjunctions to tease out different sentence follow-ons.

Finding personal pronouns invites children to discover the main personal pronouns – I, me, he, she, him, her, we, us, you, they and them – by replacing the repeated names Jenny and John in a piece of reported speech.

What is it? This activity investigates the many things that the pronoun 'it' can refer to.

Vocabulary research

This section offers a range of activities to help children become familiar and comfortable with the use of dictionaries and thesauruses. The activities involve research into the meanings and spellings of a wide range of vocabulary and into the characteristics of dictionaries, thesauruses and other books.

Make a zigzag abc picture strip: 1 and **2** provide strips of outline pictures which can be cut out and joined together (the margin ends can be glued behind adjoining strips.) Children should then be encouraged to research the words in a picture dictionary, write them in place and, finally, fold the strip into a long zigzag form.

A dictionary questionnaire asks questions about how many words a dictionary might list and prompts children to explore some of the more unusual words that might be found in it.

An unusual folding abc requires a quick glance through each alphabetical section of a dictionary to single out unusual words that attract the searcher's attention. These are then compiled into a list which can become a three-leaf folder. As an extension activity children could write the meanings of some of the unusual words on the back of the page.

The a-team is self-explanatory – a 'team' of words to be assembled, all starting with the letter 'a' but then each one followed by a successive letter of the alphabet.

A galaxy of g- words, A shower of sh- words, A q- quiz, A pick of p-creatures and **A c-feast** each have selections of words whose meanings have to be researched. All of these could be extended on the back of the page, or a new sheet of paper.

Sorting out your relations means correcting misspellings such as 'muvver' or 'farther'.

What does a thesaurus offer? shows how a thesaurus can help with finding synonym alternatives to repeated words – and to other examples of nouns, verbs and adjectives. These examples can be continued over the page.

Good and bad, In other words, From start to finish and **Extra special words** all involve simple thesaurus researching to find ranges of synonyms, often for words that are liable to be over-used.

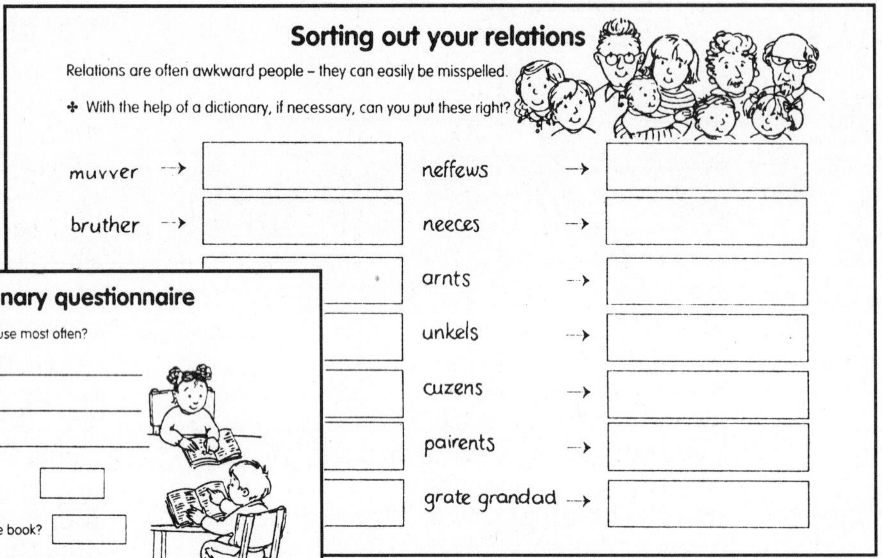
Sorting out your relations

Relations are often awkward people – they can easily be misspelled.

✣ With the help of a dictionary, if necessary, can you put these right?

muvver →
bruther →
neffews →
neeces →
arnts →
unkels →
cuzens →
pairents →
grate grandad →

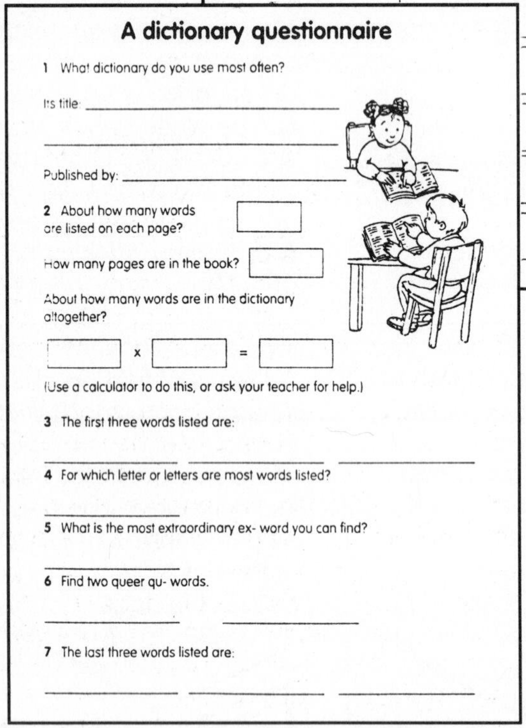
A dictionary questionnaire

1 What dictionary do you use most often?

Its title:

Published by:

2 About how many words are listed on each page?

How many pages are in the book?

About how many words are in the dictionary altogether?

× =

(Use a calculator to do this, or ask your teacher for help.)

3 The first three words listed are:

4 For which letter or letters are most words listed?

5 What is the most extraordinary ex- word you can find?

6 Find two queer qu- words.

7 The last three words listed are:

An abc of similarities is a complex investigation of synonyms and requires a considerable amount of research in a thesaurus to compile an almost complete alphabetical list of synonyms in alliterative threesomes. This activity will stretch and stimulate even the ablest pupils.

A folding abc of opposites is similar to the previous activity but seeks pairs of alliterating antonyms to be compiled in alphabetical order. This can be made into a narrow four-page folder.

What's the difference? and **One letter out – what's the difference?** both require dictionary research to sort out some homophones which are easily confused. Any further examples the children think of can be written on the back of the page.

Same words – four different meanings investigates multiple homonyms associated with 'light', 'note' and 'match'. 'Call' and 'spot' could be investigated in a similar way. Children could be asked to draw pictures to illustrate the different meanings.

The gist of a story gives a framework for investigating key words at the start of a story. As an extension children could be asked to draw a picture to illustrate a typical sentence.

Finally in this section there are two survey charts: **A part-of-speech survey** (counting and demonstrating the frequencies of the different grammatical words found in a randomly-selected dictionary page) and **A word popularity survey** (counting and demonstrating the frequencies of the ten most commonly-used English words, as found in a specimen piece of writing)..

Vocabulary selection

This section is about choosing the right words for the right occasion, encouraging correct spelling and the use of better alternatives to over-worn clichéd words. Pupils are invited to take on an editorial role, dealing with words in relevant contexts.

Greetings! provides the basis for making a greetings card and an opportunity to choose words for it.

Writing a thank-you letter asks you to choose suitable words for this type of letter and helps you to make a start.

A request letter offers a range of phrases and vocabulary that might be useful for writing this type of letter.
Questions of spelling: 1, 2 and **Questions of odd spelling** ask for choices to be made from trial alternative spellings for particular words. These three activities become progressively more difficult. A good extension for all three would be to ask children to write out the correct versions of the words on the back of the pages, without copying.
What odd 'weirds'!, Which 'weird' is it? and **Odd 'weirds' out!** also deal (in order of difficulty) with spelling choices for homophone or near homophone confusions.
Monkey's ... adventure is a story which requires decorating with suitable adjectives and adverbs.

A 'great' story asks the children to think of thirteen different alternatives to the word 'great' and to insert them in a little fishing story.
Instead of 'said' seeks alternative words for 'said' in a piece of dialogue.
Going on and on and on requires some editing of excessive 'ands' in a child's breathless report. As an extension activity, ask children to write a new version of this story.
Is it 'it's' or 'its'? Children have to choose which word to insert in the short piece of prose.

Expressive vocabulary

This section helps children to find exactly the right words – and discover new ones – for what they mean or feel.

The vocabulary discussed here is more personal – words that express sensitivity, imagination and the range of emotions. The activities provide a series of contexts with varying amounts of vocabulary back-up to encourage imaginative and poetical writing.
My mum (or alternatively My teacher or My grandmother), **My lovely pet** and **My friend** offer support in preparing simple pieces of vivid descriptive writing. Children can then be asked to write a poem or draw a picture of the subject.
On cloud nine and **Feeling sad** involve collecting appropriate happy and sad words. These are written on outline shapes (a cloud and a face) which can be cut out and hung up. (These mobiles will hang much better if a piece of card is stuck to the paper on which the poem is written.) In each case pupils should be encouraged to write a poem on the back of the page – one listing favourite activities, the other using miserable vocabulary to describe a series of calamities.

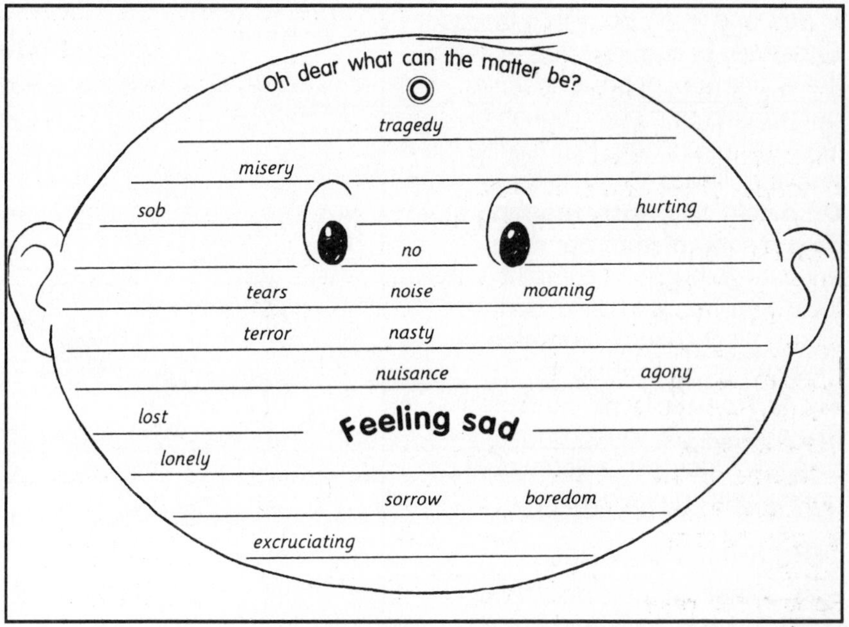

It was a dark, dark night, Fire! Fire!, Wet through and **Like a volcano** provide collections of stimulatory vocabulary on emotive subjects and have spaces (and sometimes lead-ins) for pieces of creative writing.
Like a beautiful bird has a bird shape that can be written upon (with the help of a few leading questions), coloured around the edges, cut out,

folded and hung up with a thread.
Christmas is coming! homes in on the excitement of pre-Christmas anticipation and has a series of lead-ins for children to describe the festive build-up.
On a cold and frosty morning and **Sing a song of summer days** encourage pupils to come up with their own words to describe the different sensations prompted by these weather conditions.
Yes to/No to asks for expressions of particular pleasures and disgusts. Prior discussion would be particularly helpful here.

Specialist vocabulary

Each subject or topic has its own special words or technical terms. This section gives a few indications of ways in which such vocabulary can be built up, enhancing general knowledge. The activities can be used as starting points for study of a new topic – or to develop one already underway. They can also be used, with discretion, as one-off exercises. Information and reference books will be of assistance throughout this section.
What about me? shows a detailed figure of a boy's body, which children are asked to label. This, of course, can be done at any level and with different amounts of detail. Set targets of 10, 20 or even 50 parts to be labelled. Reference and information books could be useful here.
Shapes galore has a pattern of common regular two-dimensional shapes to be labelled with the assistance of an information chart.
What shapes make up these towers? similarly deals with naming three-dimensional shapes. As an extension, children could be asked to list the names of any other 3-D shapes they know.

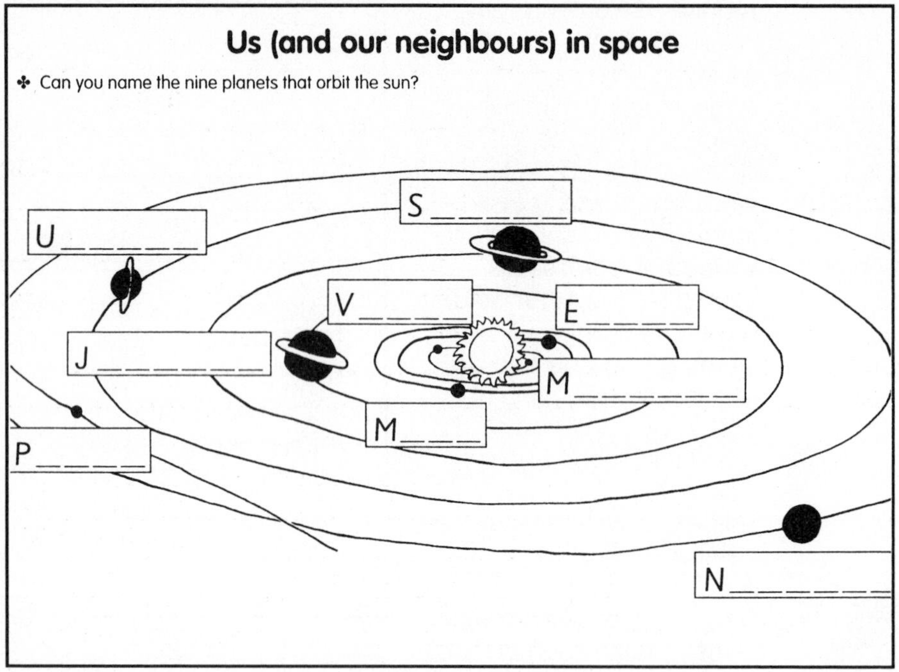

Us (and our neighbours) in space seeks basic vocabulary associated with the solar system. Extend the activity by asking children to list any other words they know which are associated with space.
Times considers words which express duration from seconds to millennia.
Flowers, fruits and vegetables involves the children in finding out and listing common plant-associated names. These lists could form a folding three-part brochure or be extended with an extra sheet of paper. Pupils should be encouraged to illustrate and identify the names they have written.

Introduce yourself to insects is a first look at the technicalities of insect life.
A zigzag selection of animals can be folded into four thin pages with another four pages available on the reverse side. The first page asks for lists of mammals, reptiles and birds, but insects, fish, dinosaurs and invertebrates can be listed on the back. Children may need guidance to recognise the different animal groups – reference material would obviously be of help.
A zigzag collection of places deals with towns, counties and countries in a similar way. Lists of rivers, seas and oceans, planets and constellations can be added to the back.
The top ten words provides a framework for compiling a glossary on any chosen subject, with the help of an information book.

Vocabulary round-up

This short concluding section takes a more general overview of words.
The first three activities **My favourite word, Amazing words** and **Crazy words** are four-page booklets. These are self-explanatory, they should be folded down the centre line and have work completed on the inside pages as directed.
New word banking uses two pages as the basis for making a little folder, like a cheque book, to collect newly-learned words (written on to special cheques).
The final page **See my skills with words** can be used as a cover for children's personal folders of vocabulary activities.

Feature grid

Features	Pages	
	Key Stage 1	Key Stage 2
adjectives	62–64, 115–117	64–65, 71, 98–99, 110
adverbs		70–71, 99, 110
alphabetical order	64, 77–80	80–81, 93–94
antonyms	26	94
apostrophes		114
articles		72–73
conjunctions		74, 113
editing		75, 107, 110–113
homonyms		97
homophones	95	95–96, 108
labelling	17–20, 34–36, 129–130	129–132, 135
letter writing		101–103
meanings		82–84, 86, 95–97, 138, 142–143
nouns	17–23, 57–59	59–61, 82–86, 98–99, 129–138
plurals	19	
poetic words		120–127
prefixes	33	39–44
prepositions	69	69
pronouns		75–76, 114
rhymes	29–31	96
roots		45–48, 56
spellings	34–36, 87	104–109
story words	16	98, 110–113
suffixes		49–52, 55–56
synonyms	89–90	88–93, 111–112
tenses	53	54, 66–67
verbs	53, 115–116	54, 66–68, 98–99, 112

Topic grid

Topics	Pages	
	Key Stage 1	Key Stage 2
animals	18, 58, 116	61, 62, 66, 85, 110, 124, 135–136
body	129	129
Christmas	125	125
days of the week	27	60
directions	69	
family	58, 115	87
food	19, 58, 134	61, 134
gifts	101	49, 102
greetings	101	
holidays	15, 23	
houses	57, 90	
months	28	60
moods		118–119, 123
night		120
numbers	25	
people	59, 115, 117	50, 59–61, 129
pets	58, 116	
places	60–61	60, 137
school	17	68
seasons		126–127
shapes	130	131
shops	19–22	
space		132
time	27–28	133
travel	15–16, 32, 69	
weather	33	122, 126
yourself		51–52

Name ____________________

A train journey

✣ Cut and fold these engines and carriages.

✣ See how many different sentences you can make from them.

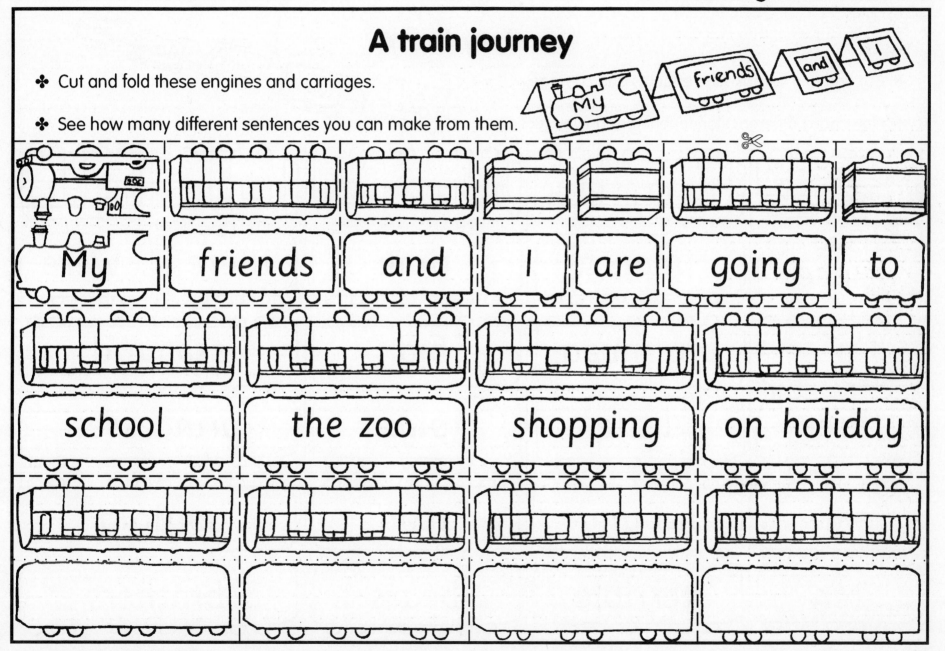

Name ________________

Making a train to start a story

A story train

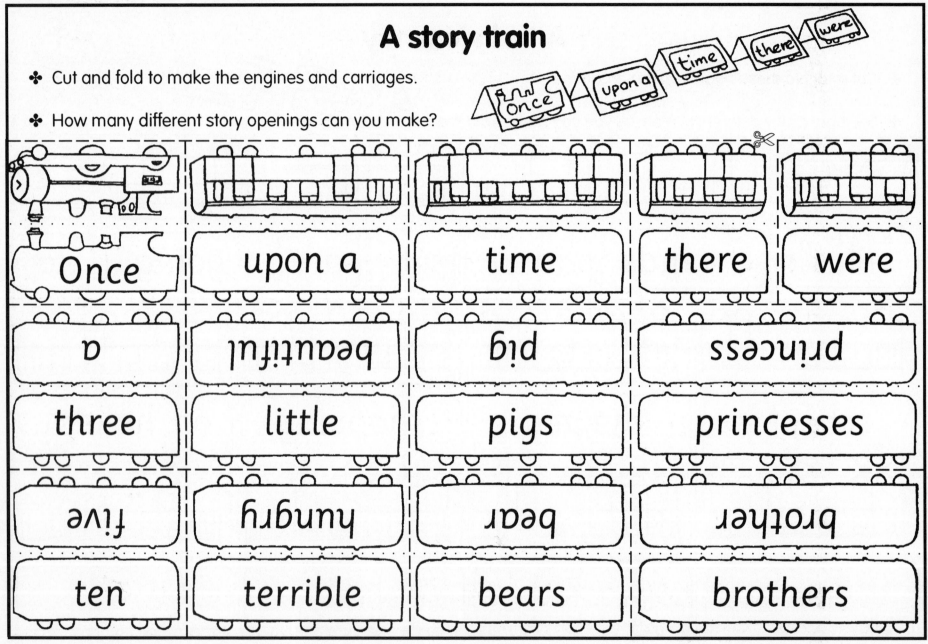

✣ Cut and fold to make the engines and carriages.

✣ How many different story openings can you make?

Name ____________________

Classroom labels

✤ Colour these, cut them out, fold and set them in the right place.

chalkboard	window	door
cupboard	table	chair
book corner	drawer	wall

Name ______________

Making and labelling some wild animals

Wild animals!

✤ Colour, cut out, fold and label these animals.

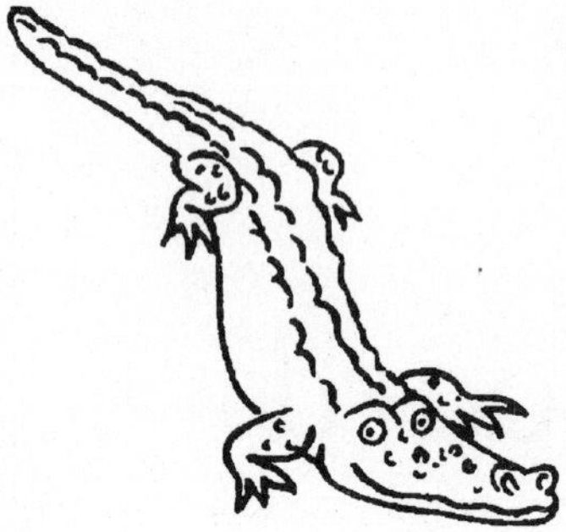

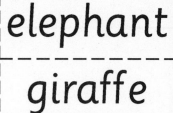

- elephant
- giraffe
- lion
- crocodile
- tiger
- monkey
- rhino
- hippo

Name ____________________

Fruit and vegetable labels

✤ Cut out these labels, add prices and set them in place.

bananas	☐
pears	☐
apples	☐
oranges	☐
pineapples	☐
potatoes	☐
carrots	☐
beans	☐
cabbages	☐
cauliflowers	☐

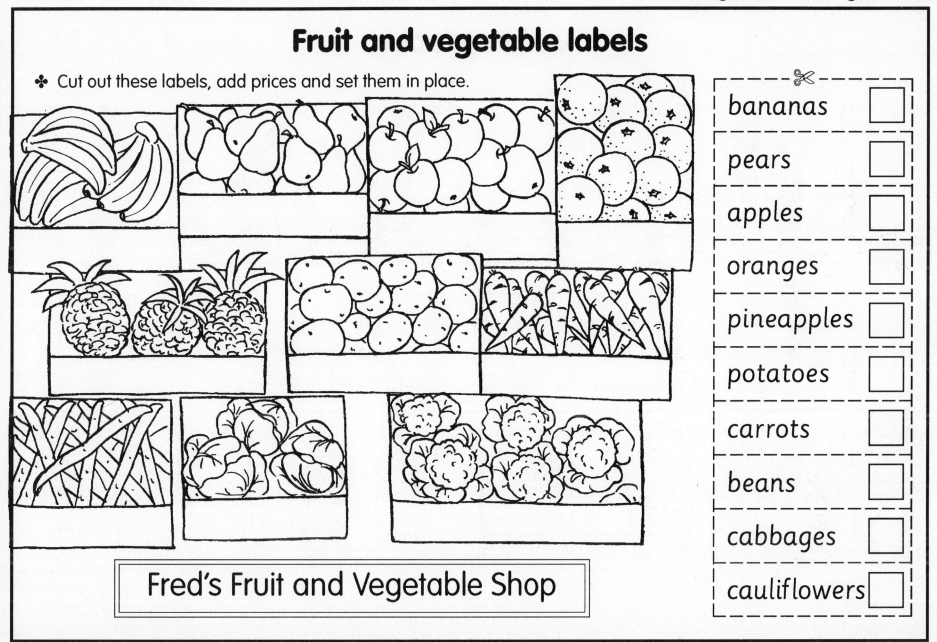

Fred's Fruit and Vegetable Shop

Name ____________________

Labelling toys

Toy shop labels

✤ Cut out the labels and put them in place.

- football game
- computer game
- dice game
- magic box
- music box
- paint box
- jumping dog
- walking penguin
- talking parrot
- teddy bear

Name ________________

A shopping game

✤ Cut out these four shopping lists and use them, with the items cut out from Shopping game: 2, to go shopping. Your teacher will tell you how.

Shopping list 1	Shopping list 2	Shopping list 3	Shopping list 4
a can of cola	a bag of crisps	a bottle of milk	a loaf of bread
a pound of carrots	a carton of juice	a packet of biscuits	a box of eggs
a bar of chocolate	a bottle of sauce	a daily newspaper	a magazine
a tin of beans	a pound of cheese	a jar of peanut butter	a bag of sugar
a box of matches	a packet of cereal	a pound of bananas	a packet of butter
a jar of jam	a box of toffees	a tin of soup	a lottery ticket

Name ________________

Shopping game: 2

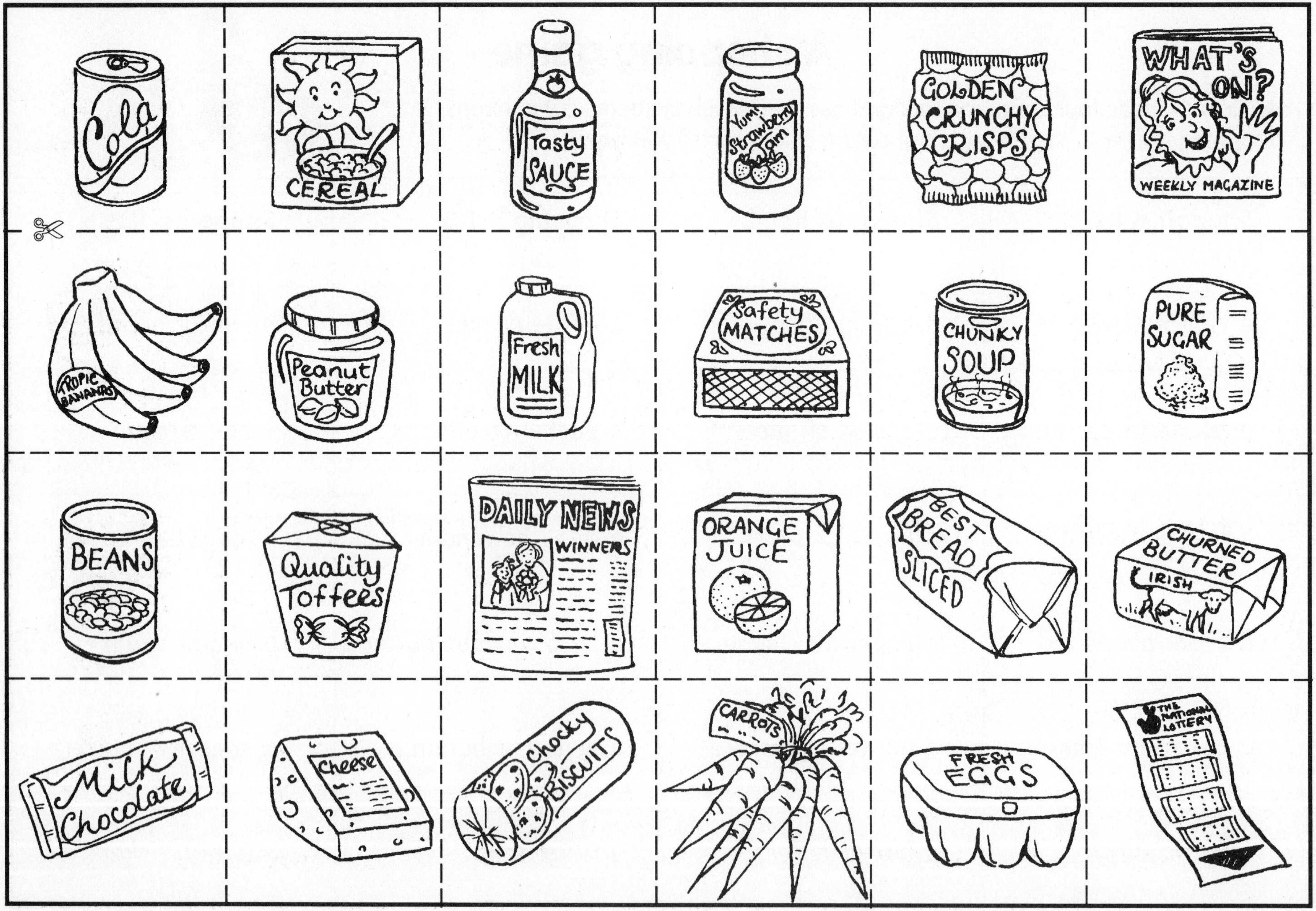

Going on holiday

Which of these would you like to take with you? You can only fit five of them in your bag.

✤ Choose the things you want, but fold the page over before you write your packing list.

1 ______________________________

2 ______________________________

3 ______________________________

4 ______________________________

5 ______________________________

← Fold under before making list.

sun-glasses

good book

camera

teddy bear

sun cap

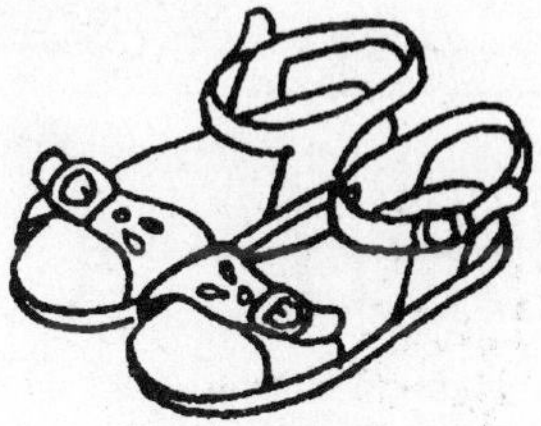

sandals

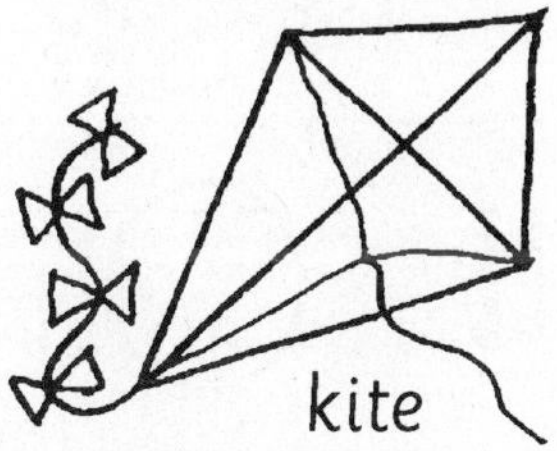

kite

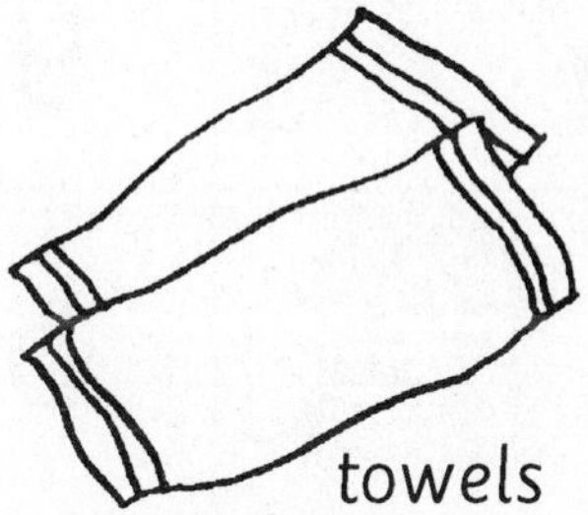

towels

sweets

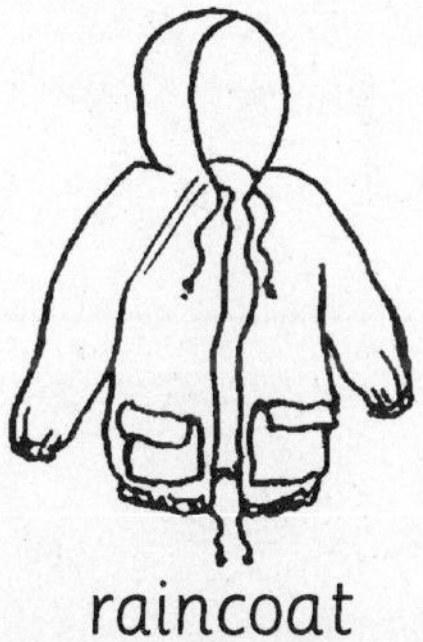

raincoat

sun cream

purse

Name ____________________

Pairing

✤ Cut out these cards and sort them into pairs, by matching the words.

car 	bell 	car	bell
bad 	cat 	bad	cat
horse 	gold 	horse	gold
house 	ball 	house	ball
boy 	good 	boy	good
dad 	dog 	dad	dog

Pairing and ordering

✤ Cut out these cards and find the matching pairs.
Then sort the words in number order.

two	ten	seven	eleven
four	seven	two	twelve
eight	eleven	one	three
twelve	nine	four	five
six	one	six	ten
three	five	eight	nine

Name ____________

Finding and playing with antonyms

Opposite sides – opposite words

- Cut out and fold these cards. Then fill in the opposite word on the back of each one.
- Ask a friend to guess the hidden opposite word.

uo			
off	down	out	under
cold	friend	left	dark
slow	back	noisy	heavy

Name ____________

Deciding on days

- ✤ Tick the correct spelling of each day, then write it in this diary.
- ✤ Cross out the ones that are wrong.

Is it Sonday, Sunday or Sundae? ____________	Visit Nan
Is it Moonday, Munday or Monday? ____________	Cubs
Is it Tewsday, Tuusday or Tuesday? ____________	Jodie's party
Is it Wendsday or Wednesday? ____________	School trip to toy museum
Is it Thirsday, Thursday or Thersday? ____________	Swimming
Is it Fryday, Firday, Friday or frieday? ____________	Sam home for tea
Is it Saturday, Satterday or Saterday? ____________	football

Name ____________

Naming the months

Calendar months

✤ Can you write the correct months on each of these calendar pages?

May	April	July	January
June	December	November	October
March	February	August	September

1

2

3

4

5

6

7

8

9
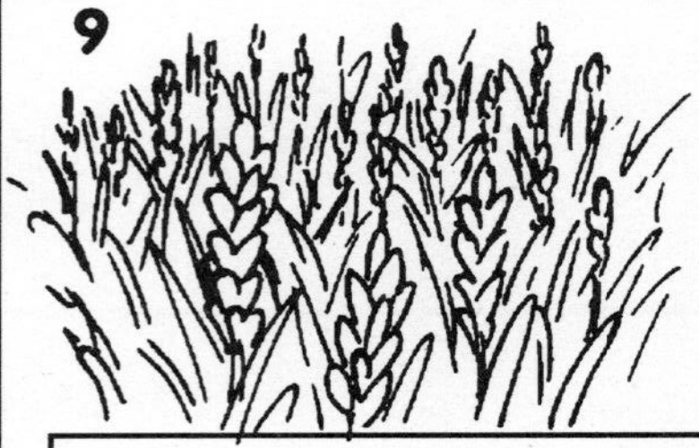

10

11

12

Name ____________________

Ten hens

✤ Fill each hen with a different -en or -end word.
The clues below should help you.

Name ____________________

Words which look and sound the same

Sound-and-look-alike words

Look at the key words in these three pictures.

✤ Can you think of six or more words that sound or look like each key word?

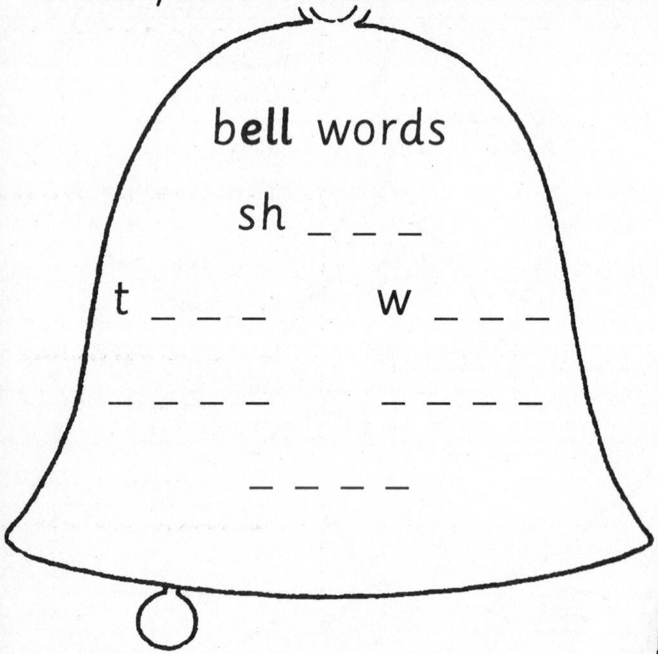

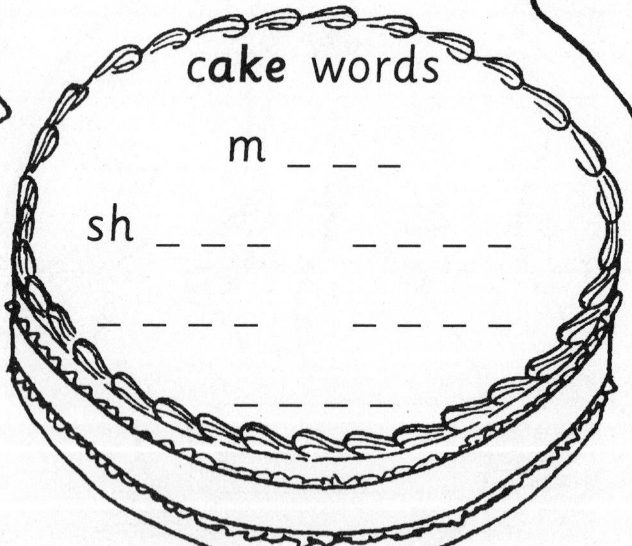

hand words

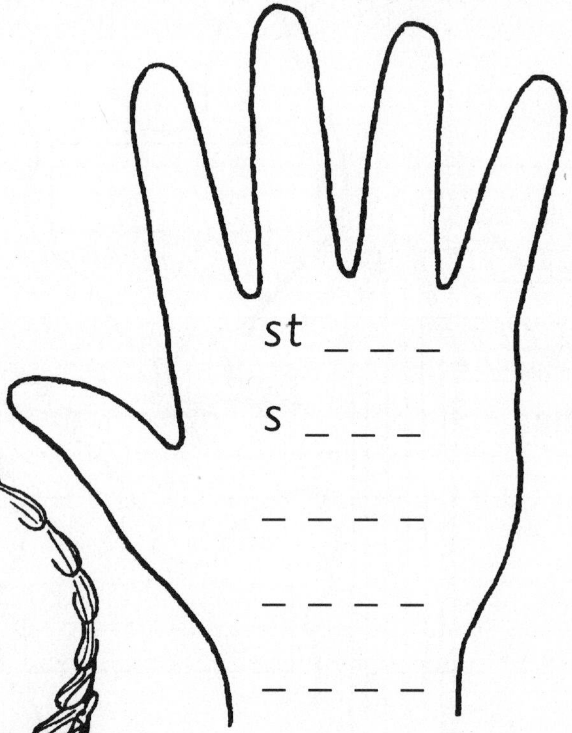

_ _ _ _

Name ____________________

Rhyme time

✤ Look at the words in the left-hand column, then work across, using the clues and the letters to fill in some words that rhyme. Be careful with the last column!

Watch out for odd spellings here! ⬇

school	t _ _ _	f _ _ _	p _ _ _	c _ _ _	r _ _ _
red	 _ _ _	T _ _	f _ _	 _ _ _ _ _	s _ _ _
bake	 _ _ _ _	l _ _ _	 _ _ _ _	m _ _ _	a _ _ _
fun	 _ _ _	 _ _ _	 _ _ _	r _ _	w _ _
fight	m _ _ _ _	 _ _ _ _ _ _	n _ _ _ _	kn _ _ _ _	k _ _ _
know	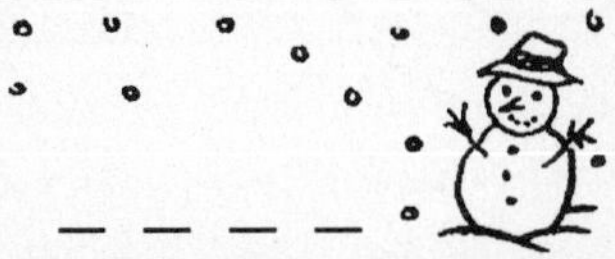 _ _ _ _	gr _ _	bel _ _	 _ _ _	n _

Name ____________

car- words

A car word-maker

✤ Cut off this side strip, cut two slits in the car and pull the strip through the slits from behind.

✤ What words can you make that start with car-?

d

t

penter

riage

ol

pet

rot

avan

Name ____________________

Sunny words

- Can you make eight different words beginning with sun- to rest on the beams?
- Colour in the sun to make it really shine and beam.

Name ____________

Label the pictures: 1

✣ Label the pictures below by writing in the names or by cutting out the word parts down the sides and sticking them in place.

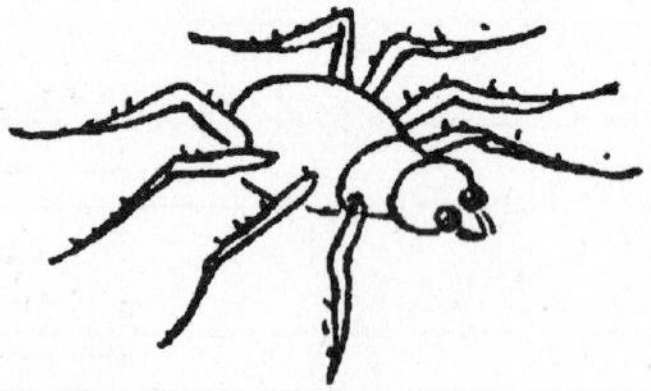

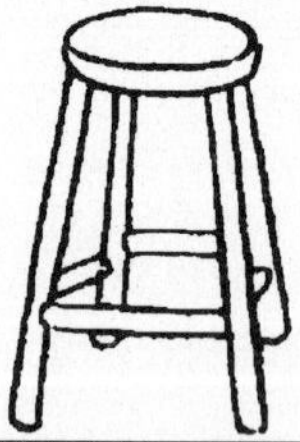

sc	arf
sp	ooter
st	hool
sc	aghetti
sp	ider
st	ade
sc	ar
sp	ool
st	amp

Name ____________________

Label the pictures: 2

✤ Label these pictures by writing in the names or by cutting out and placing the word parts in the boxes below.

- pr
- tr
- cr
- pr
- tr
- cr
- pr
- tr
- cr

- actor
- ain
- icycle
- oss
- ocodile
- ab
- am
- opeller
- ison

Name ____________________

Label the pictures: 3

✤ Label these pictures by writing in the names or by cutting out and placing the word parts in the boxes.

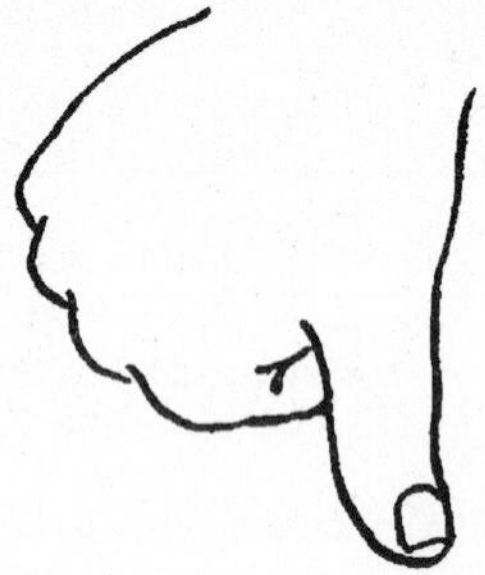

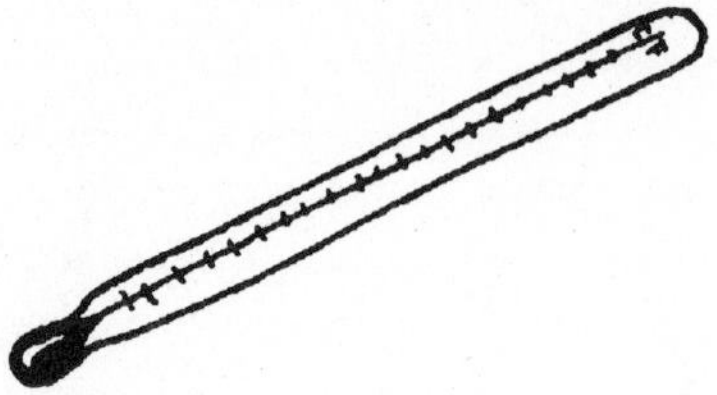

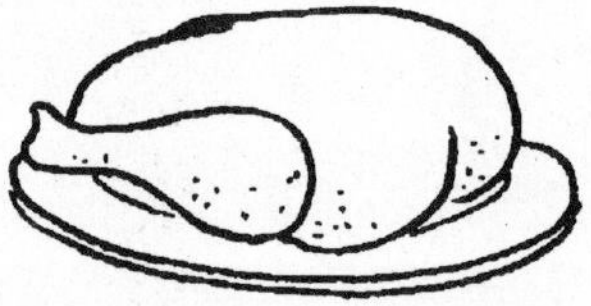

sh
ch
th
sh
ch
th
sh
ch
th

umb
istle
ermometer
ell
eep
ip
air
icken
ocolate

Name ____________________

My favourite -ing words

What do you like to do?

✤ Fill this in, using as many -ing words as you can.

The things I like doing best are:

____

____

____

____

____

and most of all, as you can see from my drawing here, I love

____

____

Do you like to...

laugh,

chatter,

sing,

eat,

drink,

go swimming

or shopping?

Perhaps you like to help or hurry or do you like to think, read, draw, dream, paint, play music, tricks or games?

Name ____________________

What am I doing all day?

✤ Answer this question with as many -ing words as you can.

Do you.....

laugh, cry, walk, talk,

sing, shout, scream, think,

stand, listen, smell, watch,

eat, drink, dream, or wait?

Name ____________________

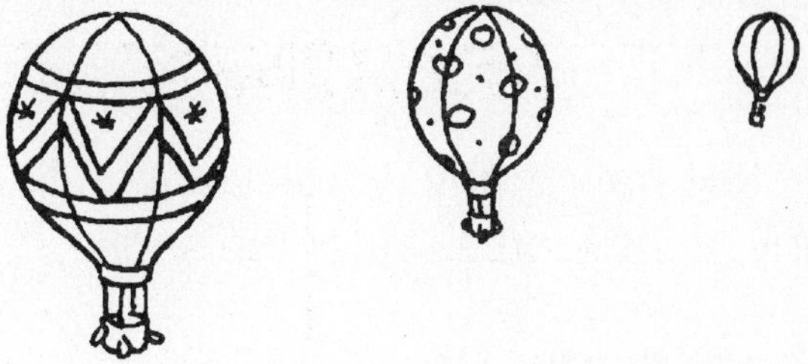

In and out

✤ How many new words can you make by joining the prefixes in- or out- to the words inside the balloon?

✤ Write the number you get in the boxes below.

in- words

____

____

____

____

____

____

____

____

____

Total ______________

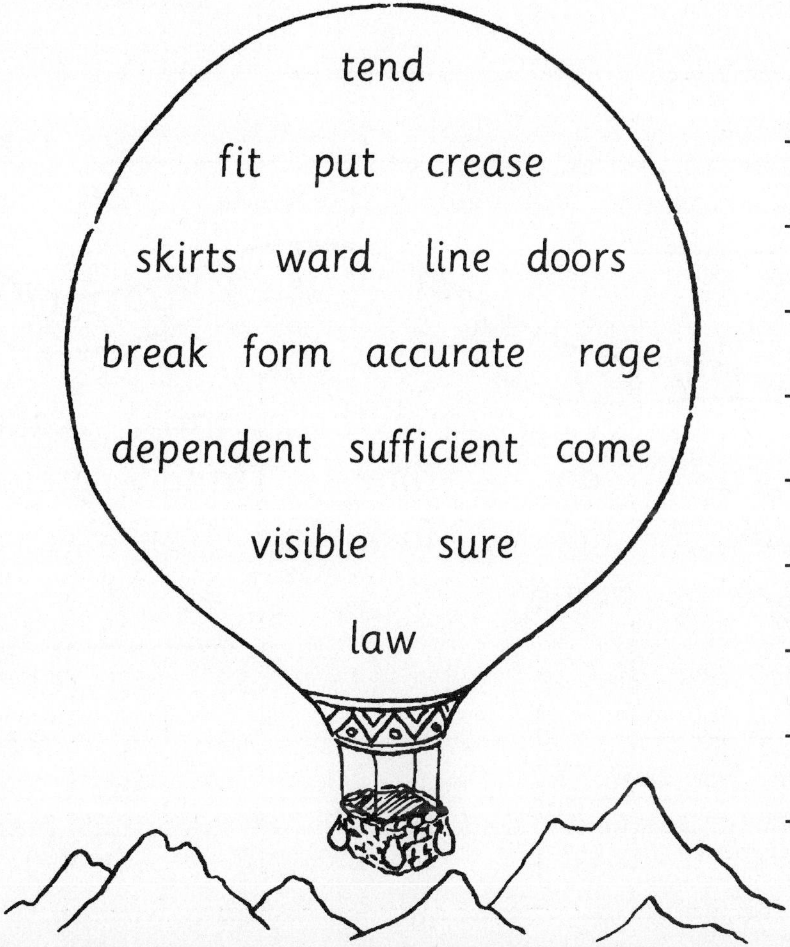

out- words

____

____

____

____

____

____

____

____

____

Total ______________

Name ____________________

Over and under

✤ See how many words you can find by joining the prefixes over- and under- to any of the words under the snake.

Over- words ________________________________

____

____

____

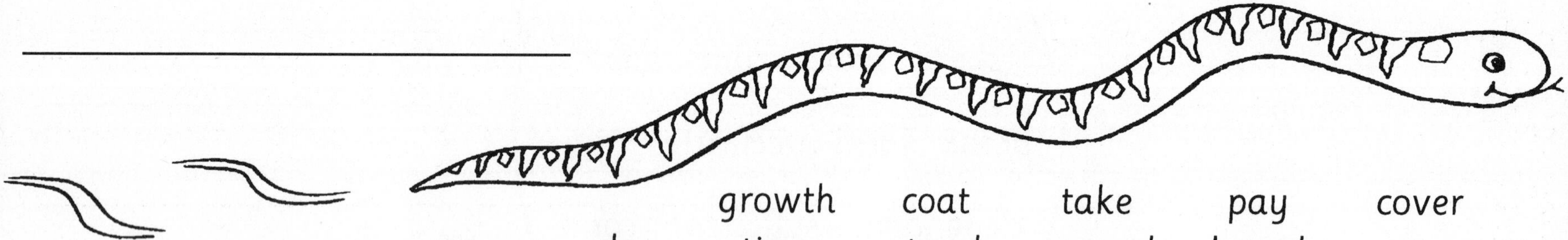

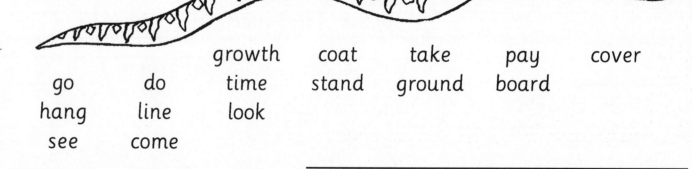

growth coat take pay cover

go do time stand ground board

joyed hang line look

head lap see come

____

Under- words ________________________________

____

____

Name ________________

Discovering

✤ Add the prefix dis- to the words below.

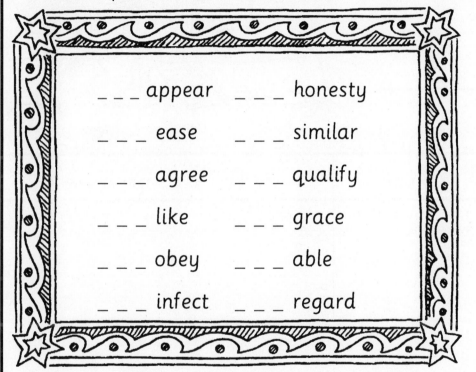

_ _ _ appear	_ _ _ honesty
_ _ _ ease	_ _ _ similar
_ _ _ agree	_ _ _ qualify
_ _ _ like	_ _ _ grace
_ _ _ obey	_ _ _ able
_ _ _ infect	_ _ _ regard

In what way did the prefix dis- change the meaning of these words?

✤ Write your answer here.

____

____

Do you understand these dis- words?

✤ Write a sentence to describe each person below.

A dishonest person ______________

____

____

A disagreeable person ______________

____

____

A disabled person ______________

____

____

A disobedient person ______________

____

____

Name ____________

un- words

Doing and undoing

✤ Try putting the prefix un- in front of these words.

_ _ kind   _ _ grateful   _ _ tidy   _ _ usual

What has changed? ______________________________

✤ Complete this chart.

A word without the prefix **un-**	The same word with the prefix **un-**	A word that has a similar meaning
like	**un**like	different
happy		
certain		
true		
safe		
clean		
exciting		
believable		

Making use of prefixes

✤ Use these prefixes to help you label the pictures.

prefix	meaning
uni-	one
bi-	two
tri-	three
tele-	far
mini-	small
micro-	very small

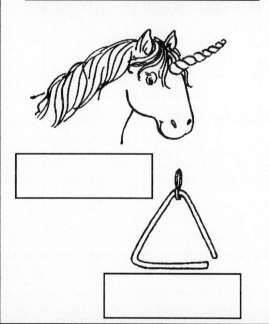

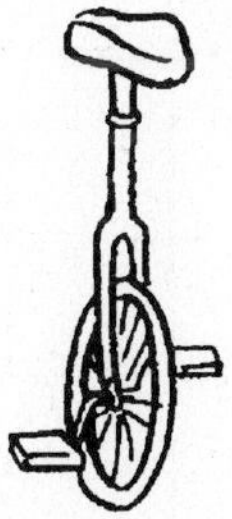

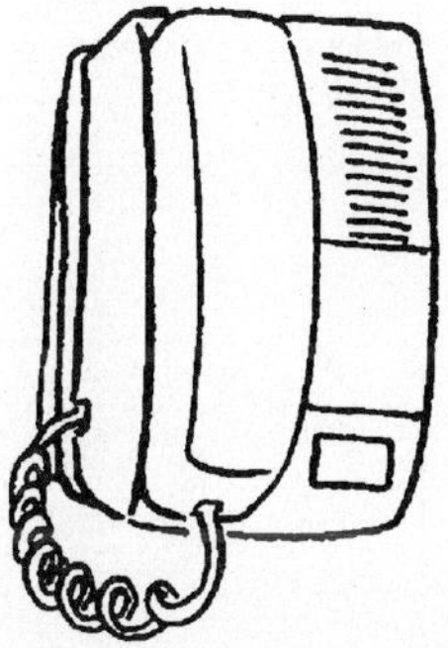

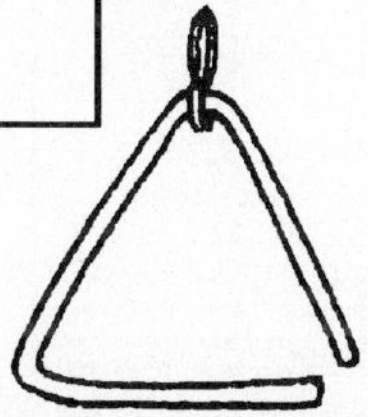

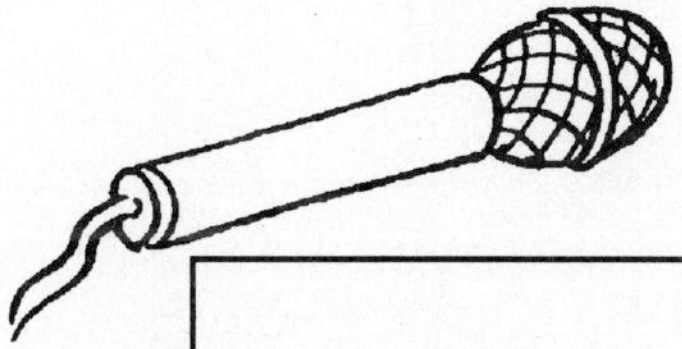

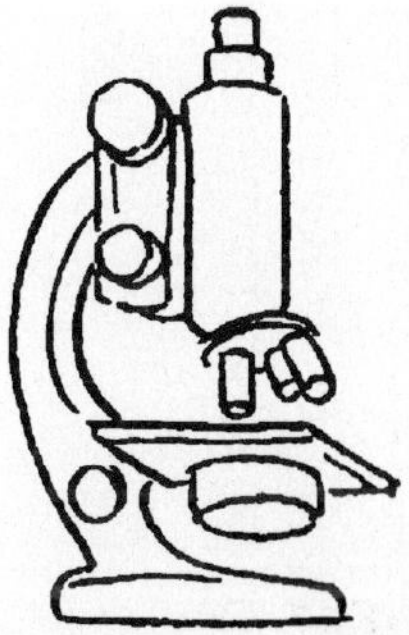

Name ____________

pre-, re- and de- words

Pre-fixing

✤ How many new words can you make by fixing de-, re- or pre- on to any of these other word parts? The first example has been done for you, but you will not be able to make three new words for each one.

fer	**pre**fer	**de**fer	**re**fer
serve	______	______	______
view	______	______	______
tail	______	______	______
cision	______	______	______
cline	______	______	______
fine	______	______	______
fix	______	______	______
scribe	______	______	______

What's the difference?

✤ Use a dictionary to help you find out what each word means – write your answers like this:

prefer means ______________

____

refer means ______________

____

defer means ______________

____

Name ____________________

Around port

✤ How many words can you report using the prefixes and suffixes shown on the boats on either side of this port?

For example: **important**

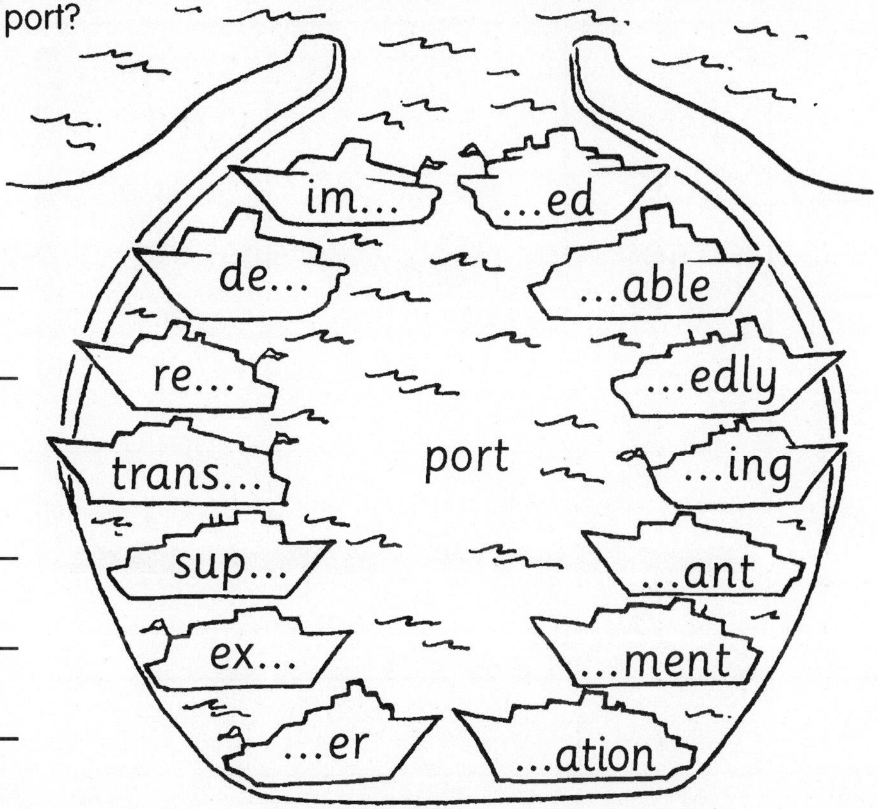

So! Do you see?
-port- is an
im**port**ant root word.
Look out for it!

Name ____________________

-form- words

Information

✤ See how many words you can form using the prefixes and suffixes on either side of the word root -form-.

For example: **information.**

per...		...ance
in...		...ed
trans...		...ation
re...	form	...ing
con...		...er
de...		...al
		...ally
		...ity

Here is a clue:

What a

____________________!

Preparations

prefix	root	suffix
in		ence
inter		ent
con	fer	e/ee
com		ed
de	par	red
re		ing
pre		ring
trans		able
		ative
		ation
		ty

✤ See how many words you can prepare around the roots -fer- and -par-.

________________ ________________ ________________

________________ ________________ ________________

________________ ________________ ________________

________________ ________________ ________________

________________ ________________ ________________

________________ ________________ ________________

✤ Write a few sentences to show that you understand some of these words.

____

____

____

Name ____________

-duct- and -struct- words

Constructions

prefix	root	suffix
in		or
intro		ory
de	duct	ion
con		ed
re	struct	ing
pro		ive
via		ible

✤ See how many words you can construct around the roots -duct- and -struct-.

✤ Write a few sentences to show the sense of some of these words.

An unbeatable gift

✤ Think of a present you would love to be given. Then think of some suitable -able words to describe it and write them on the parcel labels. (Can you squash, wash, wear, tear, kick, bend or break it?)

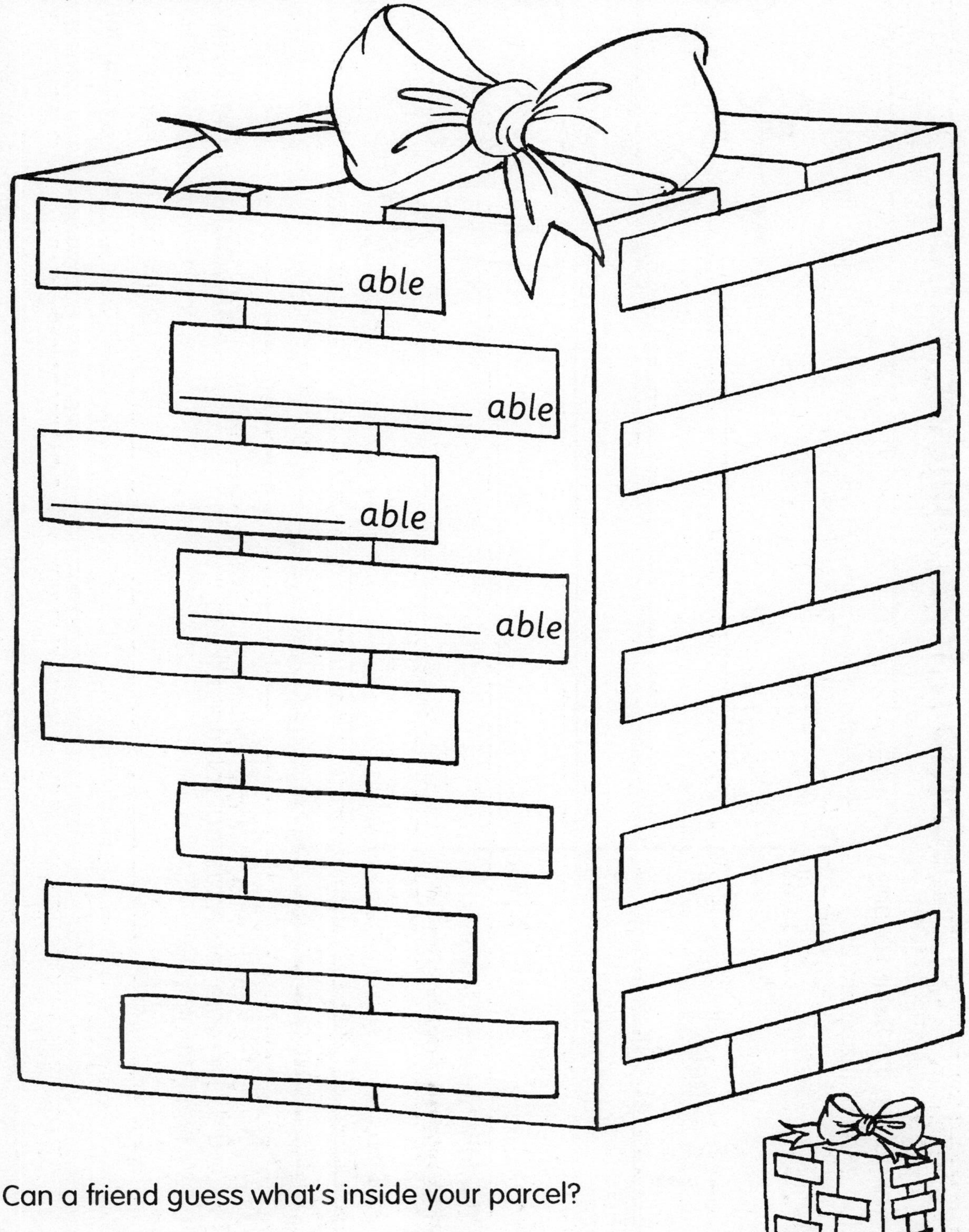

Can a friend guess what's inside your parcel?

✤ Write the answer on the back of this page.

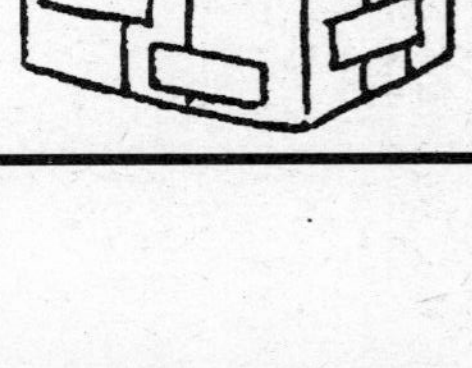

Name ____________

Become a tryer, thinker, writer...

✤ **Try** putting the suffix -er on to the ends of these words:

talk

work

help

drink

dream

listen

✤ **Think!** What kind of words do these verbs now become?

____

✤ **Write** down some of the -er words that describe you. What am I?

a writer

____

____

____

____

____

No! Not me! I'm not a guzzler!

✤ Add a few more -er words that you don't like to be (or find difficult to be).

____

____

Beware! Some letters (like n or p) double up before a suffix, like run → runner, skip → skipper.

✤ Check your -er words again!

What am I full of ?

Are you filled with beauty, delight, joy, cheer, help, tact, skill, care, or with doubt, fear, hurt, hate or even spite? All these nouns can become useful adjectives if you add the suffix -ful (please note only one **l**).

✤ Try for yourself – make your own lists of -ful words here.

How I like to be:

How I don't like to be:

Look out! y often turns to i before -ful. And be sk**i**lful with single 'l's!

✤ Check your words again!

Name ____________

Reasonableness – about yourself

Think of yourself:

Are you reasonable, lively or lazy, clever, generous, talkative, shy, quiet, tidy or untidy, friendly, rude or polite, naughty or irritable?

As you are:

✤ Add the suffix -ness to adjectives like those above to describe your own qualities.

____________ ____________

____________ ____________

____________ ____________

____________ ____________

____________ ____________

As you would like to be:

✤ Write down a few more -ness words for other qualities you would **like** to have.

____________ ____________

____________ ____________

____________ ____________

____________ ____________

____

____

Look out! y usually changes to i before -ness.

✤ Check your words again.

Going into the past

✤ Can you add **-ed** on to the end of these verbs?

I look

I watch

I wait

I call

I answer

I listen

I learn

What have you done? You changed present actions into past ones.

✤ Can you change these present actions into past ones?

You hope

You joke

You dare

You imagine

You rejoice

You chase

You race

You escape

Did you realise that verbs ending in **-e** only have a **-d** added to change them into past actions?

✤ Now put these actions into the past. (**Watch out!** Verbs ending in **b, p** or **g** often double up these letters before adding -ed or -ing.)

They skip........, hop........, trip........, shop........,

tip........, rob........, beg........, hug........, tug.......,

rub........, strip........ and stop.........

Name ____________

-ed or not? Irregular verbs

Kate's big ed-venture

Kate has just learned the rule that adding -ed to verbs turns them into past actions, but sometimes she gets carried away!

✤ Can you correct her mistakes in this story?

Kate waked (..........) very early, she getted (..........) up quietly, eated (.........) her breakfast, goed (.........) out, runned (...........) down the road and guess what she seed (...........)? A big black horse which she catched (...........) hold of. She springed (...............) up on its back, holded (.............) on tight and rided (.............) away at high speed. It taked (............) her a long way from home before she falled (............) off. She finded (.............) her way back and telled (...........) her parents. She sayed (............) she was sorry but still she was sended (............) to bed and falled (............) fast asleep.

Name ____________________

Sensationalism

✤ Make these simple words grow by adding on a variety of suffixes – sometimes two or three can be used together.

sense:	sensed	sensing	sensible	senseless
	sensation	sensational	sensationalism	
relate:				
simply:				
like:				
educate:				

Here are some suffixes you could use:

...ation
...al
...able
...ible
...er
...ing
...ed
...ment
...y
...ness
...less
...en
...ly

or think of others yourself.

Name ____________

-ion words

Simple simplification

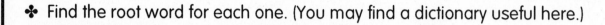

Where do all these words start from?

✤ Find the root word for each one. (You may find a dictionary useful here.)

introduction	introduce
operation	
creation	
education	
congratulations	
dedication	
regulation	
agitation	
aggravation	
preparation	
realisation	

specialisation	
serialisation	
adaptation	
quotation	
expectation	
information	
promotion	
confusion	
solution	
submission	
provision	

Name ____________

Household nouns

A noun is a word that we use as a name for a person, or an object.

✤ Fill each room in this house with a list of suitable nouns.

Things to work and play with: computer	**Things to wear and wash:** sock	**Things to think and dream about:** holidays
Things to sit on and put things on or in: drawers	**Things to look at and listen to:** doorbell	**Things to eat and drink:** biscuit

Name ______________

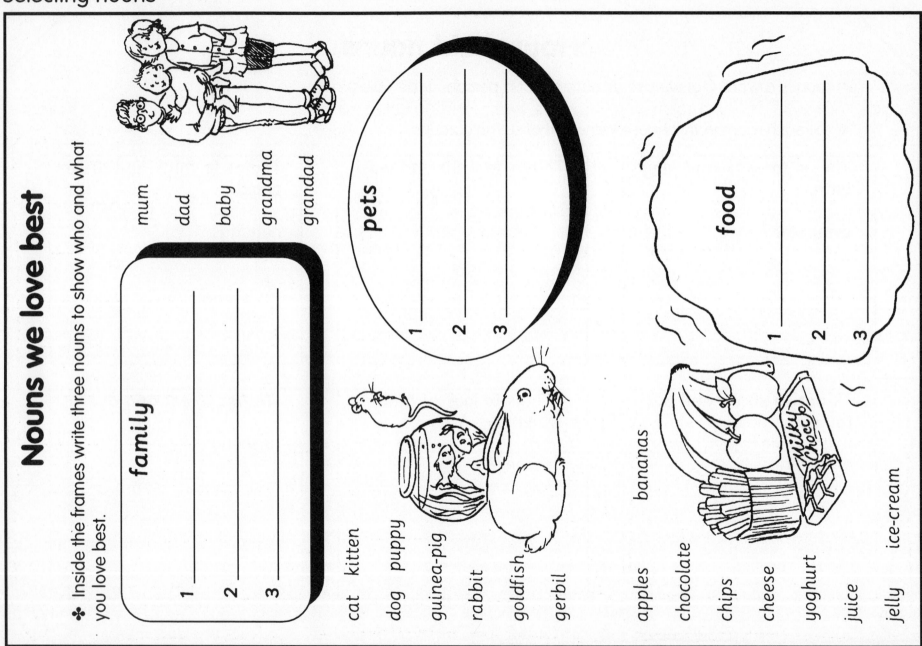

Nouns we love best

✣ Inside the frames write three nouns to show who and what you love best.

family

1 ______________

2 ______________

3 ______________

mum

dad

baby

grandma

grandad

cat kitten

dog puppy

guinea-pig

rabbit

goldfish

gerbil

pets

1 ______________

2 ______________

3 ______________

apples bananas

chocolate

chips

cheese

yoghurt

juice

jelly ice-cream

food

1 ______________

2 ______________

3 ______________

Name ____________________

A roll-call of names

It's often a good idea to register names in alphabetical order. Here's a register ready for a list of boys' names, girls' names, place names or animal names.

A ____________________

B ____________________

C ____________________

D ____________________

E ____________________

F ____________________

G ____________________

H ____________________

I ____________________

J ____________________

K ____________________

L ____________________

M ____________________

N ____________________

O ____________________

P ____________________

Q ____________________

R ____________________

S ____________________

T ____________________

U ____________________

V ____________________

W ____________________

X ____________________

Y ____________________

Z ____________________

Name ______________

Grouping nouns

The noun family

✤ Find more nouns to join this big family.

Proper nouns			Common nouns		
Place names	**Names of people**	**Days and months**	**Concrete nouns** (solid things you can touch or see)	**Abstract nouns** (things you cannot see)	**Collective nouns** (group words)
Earth	Helen	Friday	a cabbage	an idea	a flock
Great Britain	Gina	January	a king	a question	a gang
Warwick	Noel			music	

Name ____________________

Favourite animals

____

____

____

____

____

____

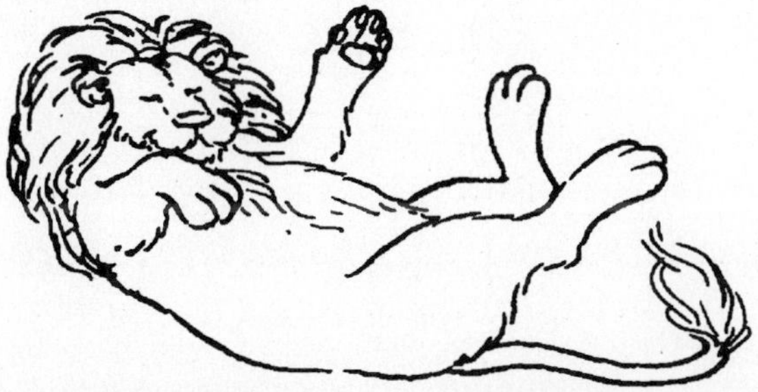

My most favourite noun of all

Page 4

Naming my favourite nouns

A four-page booklet

by ______________________________

Contents page

My favourite foods 1
My favourite people 2
My favourite places 3
My favourite animals 4

Favourite foods

____

____

____

On the pages overleaf write the names of the people and places you like best.

Page 1

Name ____________________

Adjectives for a monster

Monster adjectives

mighty large tiny happy sad miserable

green yellow blue red

✤ Think of a monster – choose some adjectives to describe it.

____

____

____

____

____

____

____

✤ Now draw it!

broad round thin tall

fierce friendly pretty ugly spotty stripy

Name ______________________

Funny faces

✤ Label each of these faces with a single word to describe how it looks to you. Look around the page for ideas!

✤ Now fill up this space by drawing and labelling some more faces.

proud	kind	tired
sleepy	weepy	ugly
mischievous	mysterious	pretty
hot	friendly	jolly
silly	hairy	happy
scared	wrinkly	clean
cheeky	angry	old
cold	cheerful	spotty
dirty	sad	cross
thin	plump	hungry
suspicious	worried	miserable

Name ____________

An a to z of adjectives

Amazing zany things

✤ Can you find two adjectives beginning with each letter of the alphabet to describe all sorts of things?

awful,	annoying	things	m		things
b	b	things	n		things
c		things	o		things
d		things	p		things
e		things	q		things
f		things	r		things
g		things	s		things
h		things	t		things
i		things	u		things
j		things	v		things
k		things	w		things
l		things	y or z		things

Name ____________________

How I think

My adjectives for –

football: ____________________

school: ____________________

good food: ____________________

nuisances: ____________________

swimming: ____________________

summer: ____________________

snow: ____________________

My favourite adjective – the one I use most:

Page 4

My favourite adjectives

A four-page booklet

by ____________________

Contents Page

Me: describing myself 1
My family and friends 2
(For example: My mum is tall and twinkly)
My toys and pets 3
(For example: My bike is ________ and ________)
How I think 4

Me

I look ____________________

I feel ____________________

Sometimes I am ____________________

Just occasionally I am ____________________

Page 1

Name ____________________

Cat and mouse verbs

What did the cat do with the mouse?

✤ Can you think of eight actions (verbs) that the cat might have done with the mouse?

The cat **sniffed** the mouse.

The cat ____________________ the mouse.

The cat ____________________ the mouse.

The cat ____________________ the mouse.

The cat ____________________ the mouse.

The cat ____________________ the mouse.

The cat ____________________ the mouse.

The cat ____________________ the mouse.

✤ Now can you think of eight actions (verbs) the mouse might have taken?

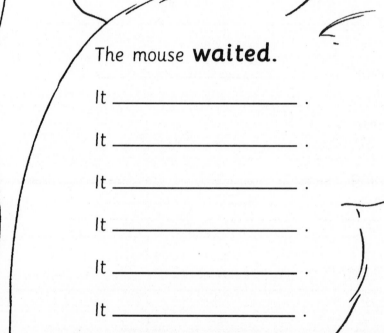

The mouse **waited.**

It ____________________ .

It ____________________ .

It ____________________ .

It ____________________ .

It ____________________ .

It ____________________ .

It ____________________ .

Name ______________

What do they do?

✤ Can you write at least three things that each of these people, animals or objects do? (You will need to think of three verbs to go with each of the plural nouns.)

Babies ______________ ______________ and ______________ .	Computers ______________ ______________ and ______________ .	Birds ______________ ______________ and ______________ .
Grandparents ______________ ______________ and ______________ .	Cars ______________ ______________ and ______________ .	Helpers ______________ and ______________ ______________ .

Name ____________

Choosing verbs

What others do

Teachers like to ____________

____

Parents like to ____________

____

Friends like to ____________

____

Babies like to ____________

____

Dogs like to ____________

____

My most favourite verb of all

Page 4

My favourite verbs

A four-page booklet by ____________

Contents Page

What I do at school	1
What I do outside school	2 and 3
What others do	4

What I do at school

____

____

____

____

Page 1

Name ____________________

Which way is it?

✤ Can you give Anwar directions to get from home to school?

1 Out of the house ____________________

2 Down ____________________

3 ____________________

4 ____________________

5 ____________________

6 ____________________

7 ____________________

8 ____________________

9 ____________________

10 ____________________

Is it down, up, under, over, right, left, past, straight on, along, across, beside, through, in, on or out?

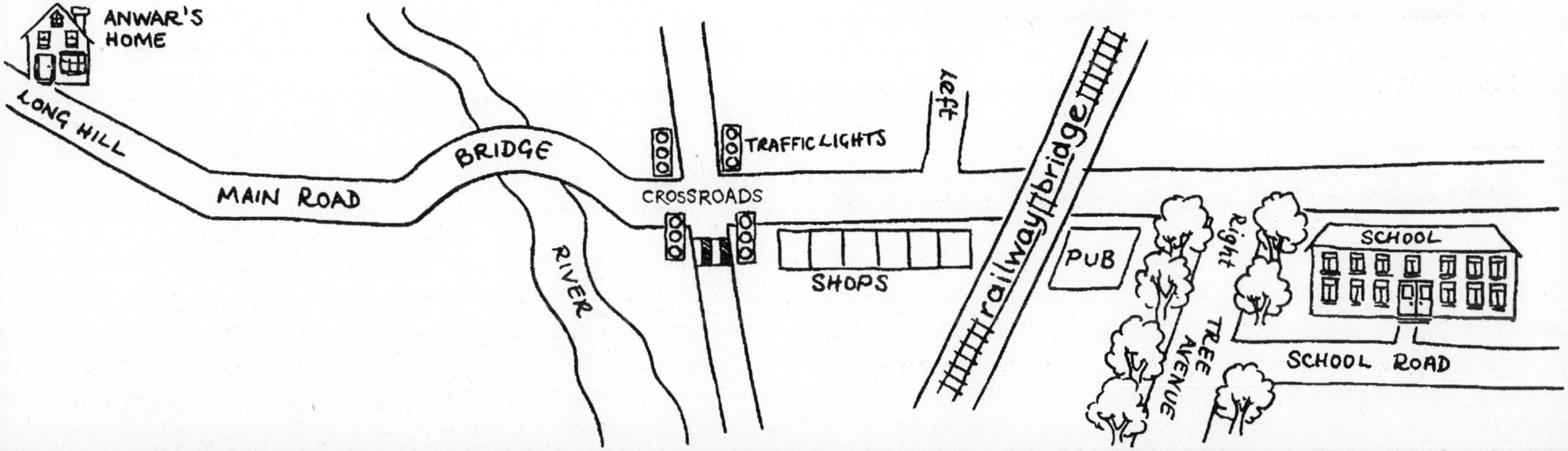

Name ____________________

Using adverbs advisedly

✤ Find suitable adverbs to describe each of these actions. Look around the page for ideas.

freely eagerly deftly carefully boldly

avidly zealously wisely valiantly thoughtfully softly

get up	**go**	**listen**
____________	____________	____________
wait	**act**	**speak**
____________	____________	____________
behave	**play**	**continue**
____________	____________	____________

loudly kindly joyfully intently happily gracefully

roughly quietly patiently oddly nicely mysteriously

Name ____________

Tremendously revealing comments

✤ Use some of the adverbs and adjectives from this page, or any others you can think of, to express how you feel about the following things.

My friends are ______________________________ .

My family is ______________________________ .

My street is ______________________________ .

My class is ______________________________ .

My work is ______________________________ .

My appearance is ______________________________ .

My behaviour is ______________________________ .

The weather is ______________________________ .

The world is ______________________________ .

What a ______________________________ day!

absolutely	*slightly*
incredibly	*extremely*
strangely	*occasionally*
always	*totally*
quite	*hysterically*
hardly	*extraordinary*
calm	*dull*
exciting	*enjoyable*
interesting	*disappointing*
surprising	*ghastly*
infuriating	*wonderful*
funny	*happy*
clever	*rude*

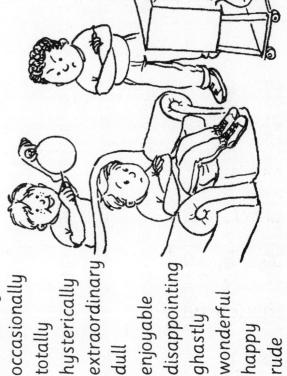

Investigating articles

These three words are called articles: **the** **an** **a**

✤ Answer the questions below to find what is special about them.

1 Do articles make sense when used all on their own? Yes/No

2 What kinds of words do articles usually introduce? ____________

3 Which of the three words is the definite article (the most precise one)? ____________

4 Which ones are indefinite (the more general ones)? ____________

5 When do we use 'an' instead of 'a'? Before ____________ .

6 Can you insert suitable articles to make sense of this article about articles? (The word 'article' has a lot of different meanings!)

Genuine articles

.... article can be genuinely one of several things. When we get up in .... morning we put on articles of clothing. When we set off down .... road to school we carry various articles (assorted objects) in our bags. We also read articles – pieces of writing in magazines. When we talk or write we use them all .... time – special words like ...., ... or .... But when we talk about '.......... genuine article' this expression means .... real thing – not .... fake!

Investigating more articles

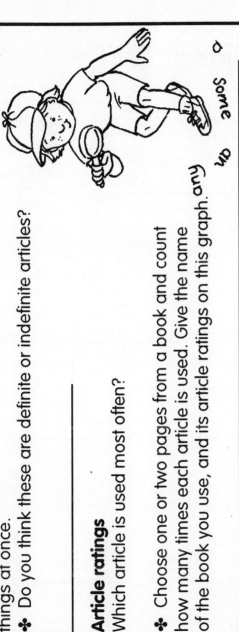

Any more articles?
'Any' and **'some'** also act as articles when we want to introduce several things at once.

✣ Do you think these are definite or indefinite articles?

____

Article ratings
Which article is used most often?

✣ Choose one or two pages from a book and count how many times each article is used. Give the name of the book you use, and its article ratings on this graph.

Name of book: ______________________ pages ____ – ____

numbers of times used					
12					
11					
10					
9					
8					
7					
6					
5					
4					
3					
2					
1					
	a	an	any	some	the

Name ______________________

Join in with conjunctions

A conjunction is a word used to join parts of a sentence. Look at the range of sentences you can make when you 'look carefully' and use different conjunctions.

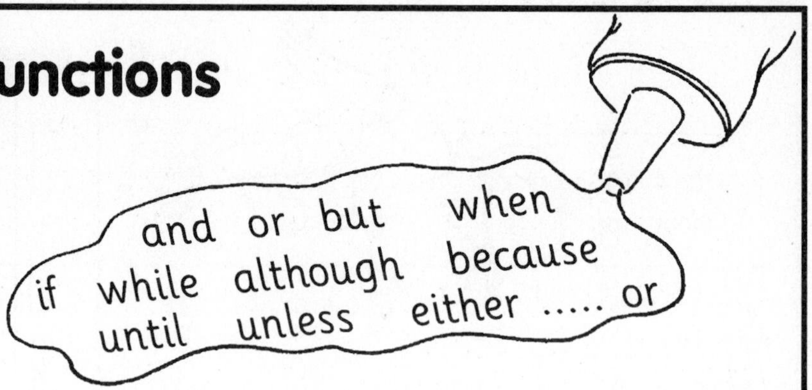

✤ Finish these sentences in as many ways as you can.

Look carefully and ____.

Look carefully or ____.

Look carefully when ____.

Look carefully if ____.

Look carefully although ____.

Look carefully unless ____.

Look carefully because ____.

Look carefully but ____.

Look and keep looking until ____.

Finding personal pronouns

✤ Can you improve this piece of writing by replacing most of the repeated names with personal pronouns? The first few lines have been done for you.

John and Jenny

John and Jenny were best friends. ~~John~~ He always went around with ~~Jenny~~ her, and she ~~Jenny~~ never left ~~John~~ him. ~~John and Jenny~~ They loved just playing and chatting endlessly.
'Do Jenny like that music?' John would say.
'Jenny think it's brilliant,' Jenny would reply.
'Did John finish your crisps? Give some to Jenny!' Jenny would cry.
'John have none left,' John would say sadly.
'What shall Jenny and John do now?' Jenny and John would often wonder.
'Let's hide so that no one will find Jenny and John.'
So that is what Jenny and John did, both of Jenny and John. Jenny and John would then disappear for hours.

You should have found that there are eleven different basic personal pronouns.

✤ Write each one again in these boxes.

Name ____________________

What is it?

See for yourself what an amazing variety of things the word 'it' can stand for.

✤ Think of words to replace 'it' in the boxes below.
It can be the name of a place like

London or

It can be something to eat like

or

It can be something to play with like

or

It can be something we like to look at like

or

Or it can be invisible like

or

It may be something the matter like a

headache or

or it may be a little idea like

or

But it may well be totally different like

[ ]

or

[ ]

or even

[ ]

A tricky question
What does 'it' stand for when we say 'It is raining'? Don't worry if you are not sure of the answer – nobody else is, not even a language expert.

Make a zigzag abc picture strip: 1

✤ Label the pictures on these two pages with the help of a picture dictionary. Colour them, then cut out the strips, fold them and join them together.

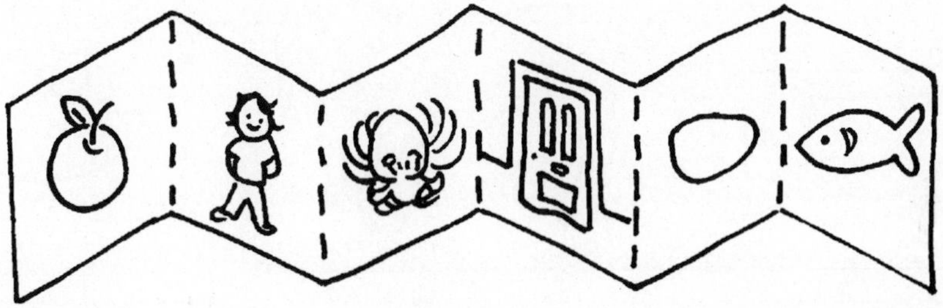

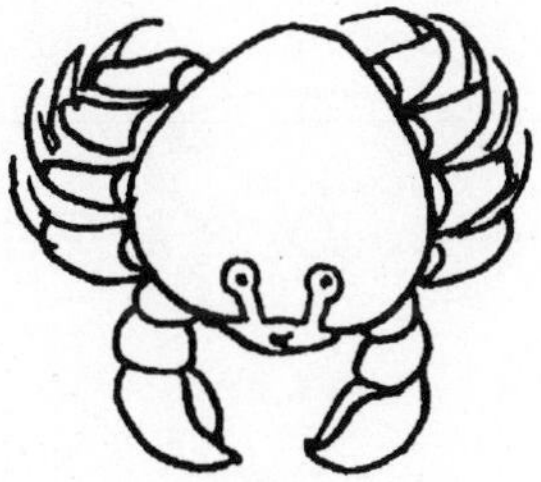

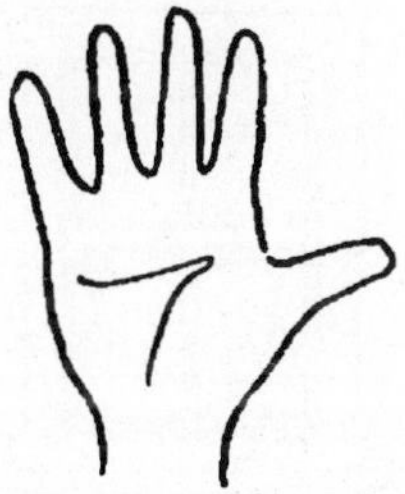

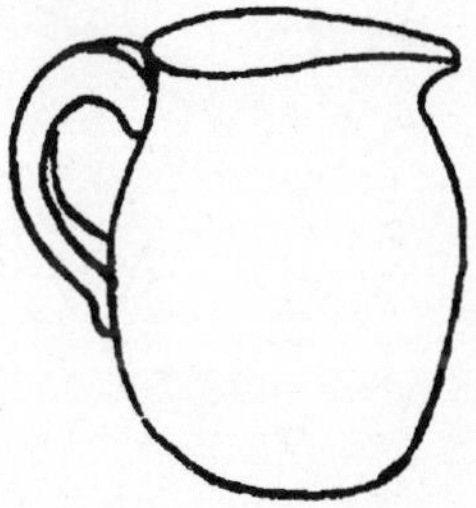

Name ____________________

A picture dictionary: 2

Make a zigzag abc picture strip: 2

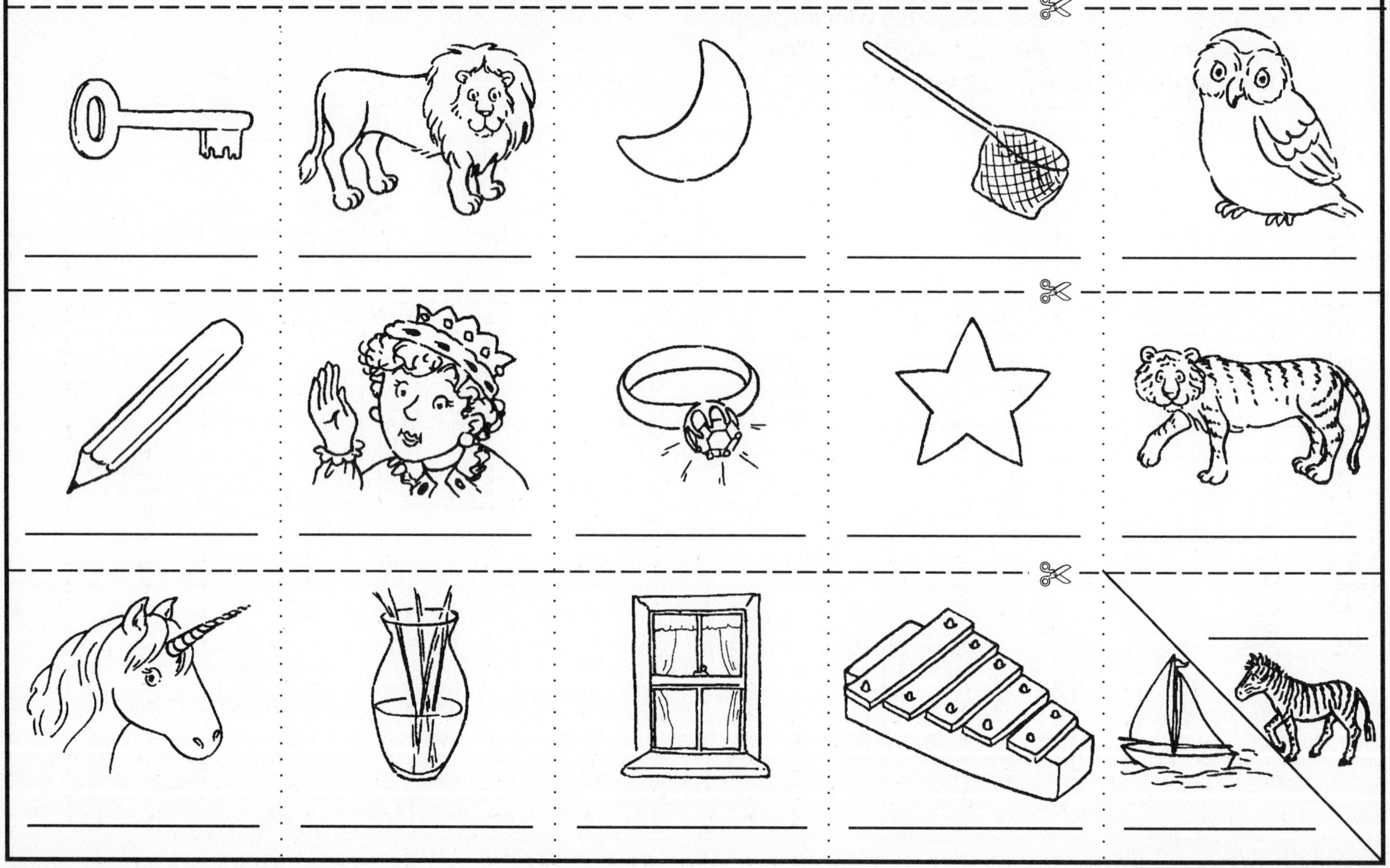

A dictionary questionnaire

1 What dictionary do you use most often?

Its title: ____________________

____

Published by: ____________________

2 About how many words are listed on each page? [ ]

How many pages are in the book? [ ]

About how many words are in the dictionary altogether?

[ ] × [ ] = [ ]

(Use a calculator to do this, or ask your teacher for help.)

3 The first three words listed are:

__________ __________ __________

4 For which letter or letters are most words listed?

____

5 What is the most extraordinary ex- word you can find?

____

6 Find two queer qu- words.

__________ __________

7 The last three words listed are:

__________ __________ __________

Name ____________

Looking for unusual words

An unusual folding abc

✤ Glance through your dictionary and choose an unusual word which starts with each letter of the alphabet.

✤ List them here.

a ____________

b ____________

c ____________

d ____________

e ____________

f ____________

g ____________

h ____________

i ____________

j ____________

k ____________

l ____________

m ____________

n ____________

o ____________

p ____________

q ____________

r ____________

s ____________

t ____________

u ____________

v ____________

w ____________

x ____________

y ____________

z ____________

The a-team

Did you know that 'a' is the only letter which can be followed by every other letter of the alphabet, including itself?

✤ Use your dictionary to help you find examples to make up the full a-team.

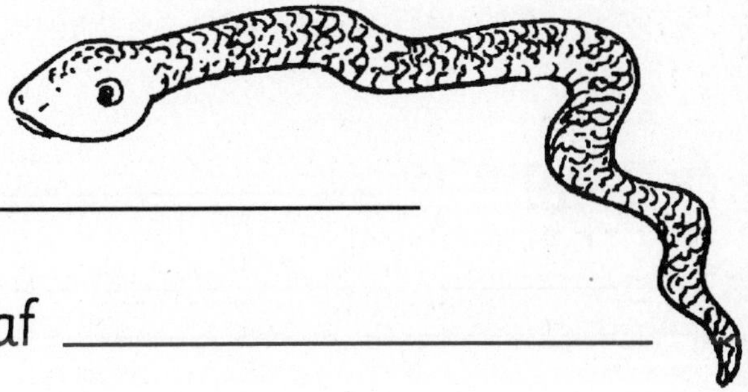

aardvark   ab ______________   ac ______________

ad ______________   ae ______________   af ______________

ag ______________   ah ______________   ai ______________

ajar   akimbo   al ______________

am ______________   an ______________   aorta

ap ______________   aq ______________   ar ______________

as ______________   at ______________   au ______________

av ______________   aw ______________   ax ______

ay ______________   az ______________

Looking up g-words

Name ____________

A galaxy of g-words

✤ Use your dictionary to find the meaning of these g- words.

A gaggle is ____________________

____

A garment is ____________________

____

A gazelle is ____________________

____

A gnat is ____________________

____

✤ Draw and label three of these g- words.

A geyser is ____________________

____

A germ is ____________________

____

A gong is ____________________

____

A gullet is ____________________

____

A galaxy is ____________________

____

Name ____________________

A shower of sh- words

✤ Use a dictionary to help you explain what is inside each of these droplets.

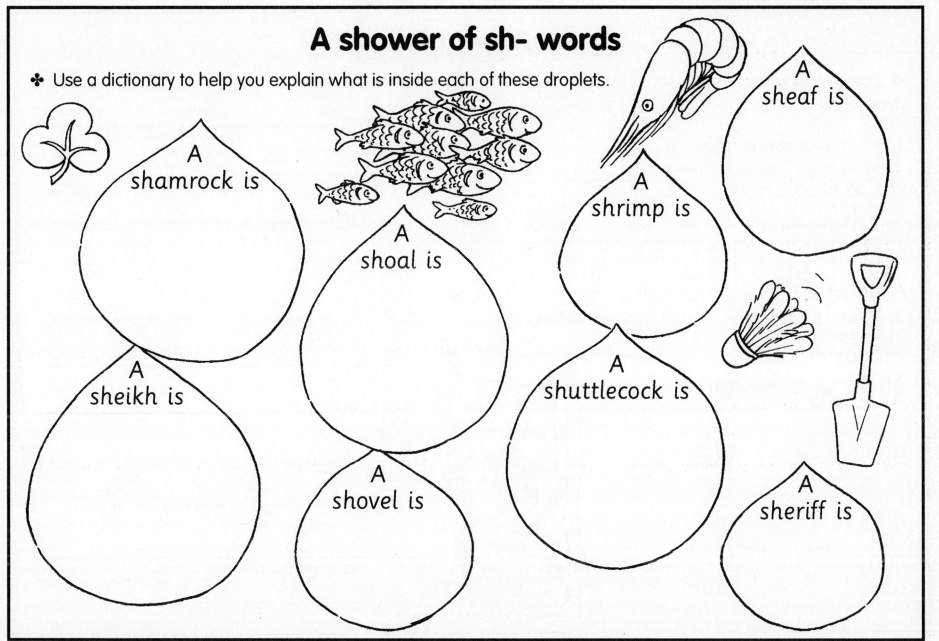

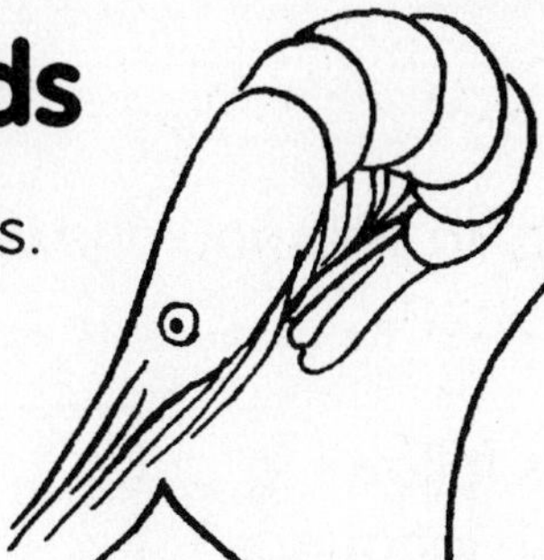

A sheaf is

A shamrock is

A shoal is

A shrimp is

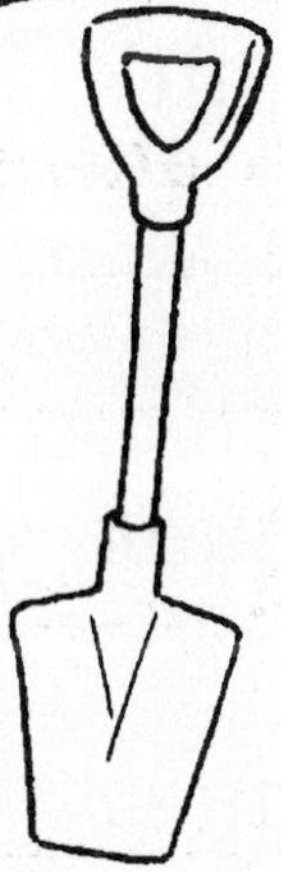

A sheikh is

A shuttlecock is

A shovel is

A sheriff is

Name ____________________

A q- quiz

✤ Use your dictionary to help you answer these questions.

1 What letter always follows 'q' in words in the English language? ☐

2 What are the only four letters that can follow 'qu'?

qu☐ qu☐ qu☐ qu☐

3 What is the last letter needed to complete each of these words?

quac	quit
queu	quak
quie	quic
qui	quain

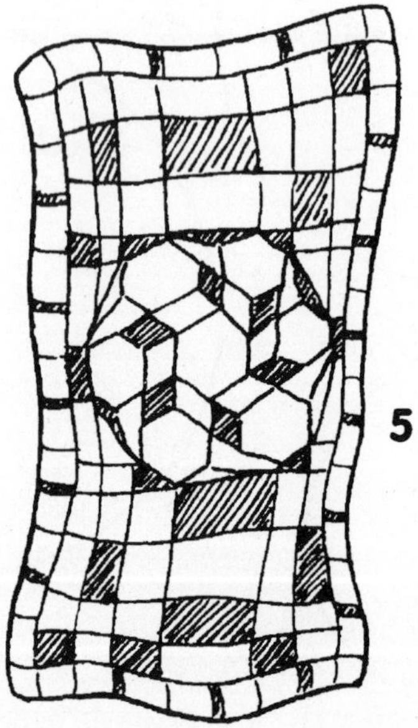

4 What are these?

A quarry is ____________________

____

A quay is ____________________

____

A quilt is ____________________

____

A quartet is ____________________

____

5 What other quaint qu- words can you find?

____

____

Name ____________

A pick of p- creatures

✤ Use your dictionary to help you write (and sometimes draw) something that is special about each of these creatures.

A panda ____________

____

____

A peacock ____________

____

____

A puma ____________

____

____

A piranha ____________

____

____

A pheasant ____________

____

____

A porcupine ____________

____

____

A pterodactyl ____________

____

____

Name ____________

Looking up c- food words

A c- feast

Lots of things which are good to eat begin with the letter c.

✤ Use your dictionary to help explain what these are.

cheese is ____________________________

____

chocolate is ____________________________

____

caramel is ____________________________

____

chips are ____________________________

____

cherries are ____________________________

____

cauliflower is ____________________________

____

candy is ____________________________

____

coconut is ____________________________

____

cream is ____________________________

____

Name ______________

Sorting out your relations

Relations are often awkward people – they can easily be misspelled.

✤ With the help of a dictionary, if necessary, can you put these right?

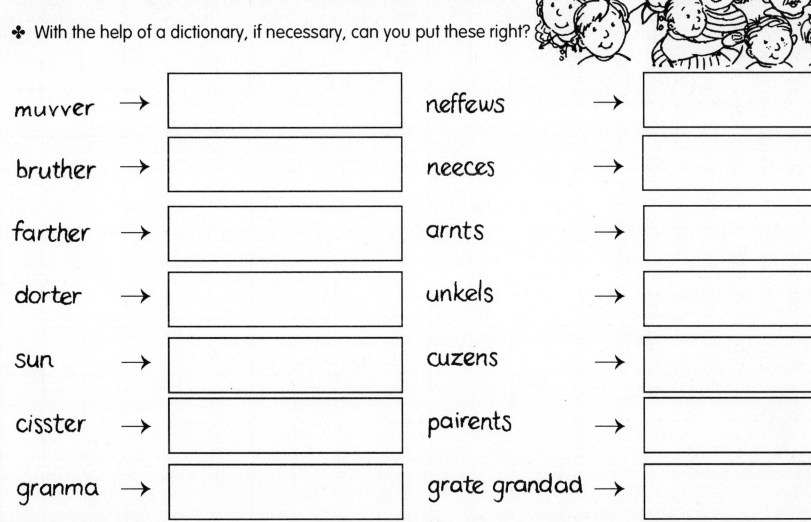

muvver →		neffews →	
bruther →		neeces →	
farther →		arnts →	
dorter →		unkels →	
sun →		cuzens →	
cisster →		pairents →	
granma →		grate grandad →	

Name ____________________

What does a thesaurus offer?

✤ Read the sentences below. Look out for the marked words!

A thesaurus offers a long list of words in alphabetical order. With each word it also offers[1] a list[2] of synonyms – different words with similar meanings. It gives us a chance to use a variety of suitable words for every occasion. It also gives[3] us a chance[4] to avoid repeating the same word[5] too often.

✤ Use a thesarus to find more suitable[6] words for those marked with numbers.

1 ____________________ **2** ____________________

3 ____________________ **4** ____________________

5 ____________________ **6** ____________________

✤ Fill in some examples of thesaurus entries; use words which have five or more synonyms.

A noun (n.): ____________________ Its synonyms: ____________________

____

____

An adjective (adj.): ____________________ Its synonyms: ____________________

____

____

A verb (vb.): ____________________ Its synonyms: ____________________

____

____

Name ____________

Good and bad

✤ Use a thesaurus and a dictionary to find and write in as many different words as you can that are similar in meaning to the words 'good' and 'bad'.

good

bad

Name ______________

Looking up synonyms

In other words

✤ Find and list, with the help of a thesaurus, a number of words which have similar meanings to these four.

hard

high

home

happy

Name ______________

From start to finish

✤ Move along this racetrack by finding, with the help of a thesaurus, four words which have a similar meaning to each of those given on the track.

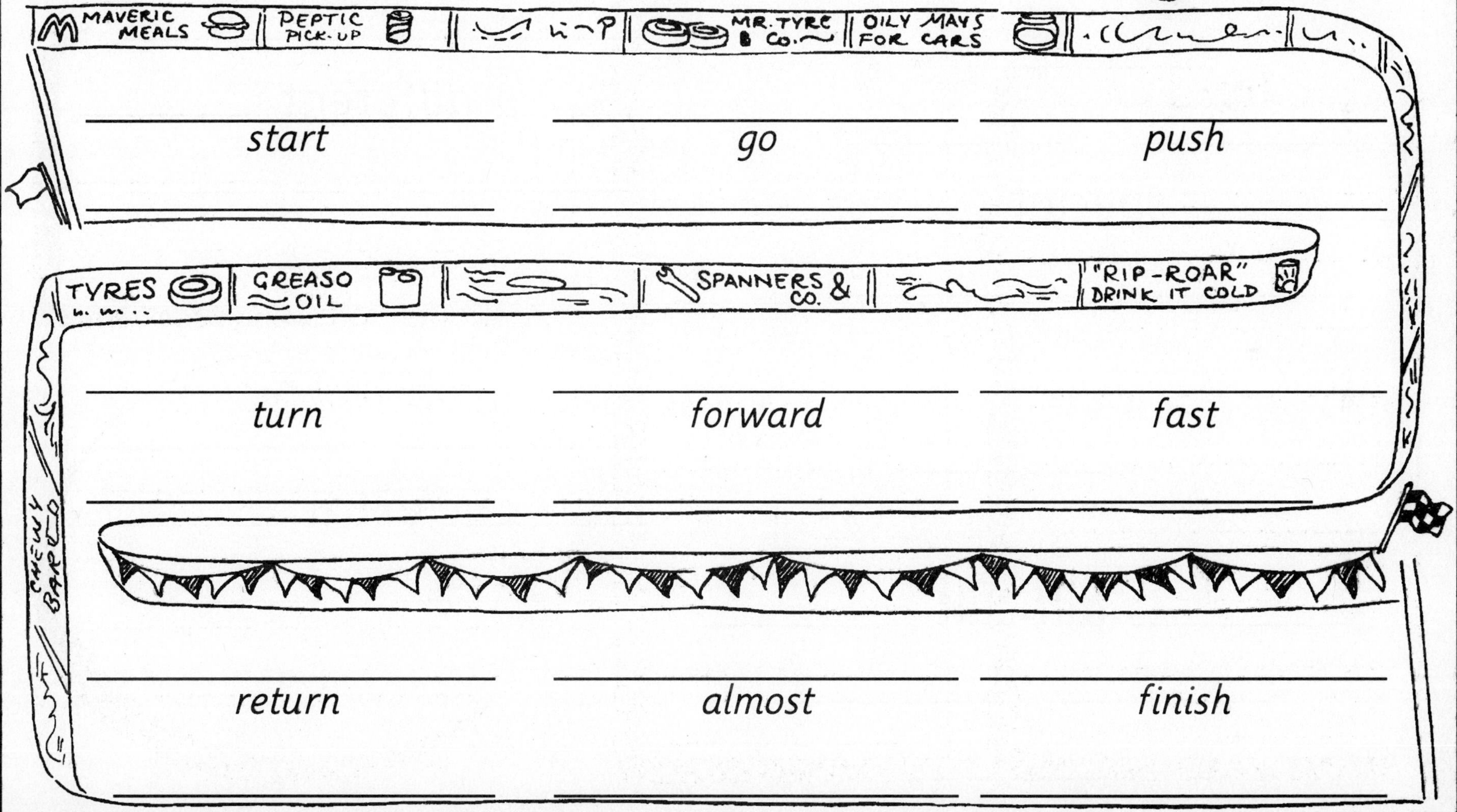

start	*go*	*push*
turn	*forward*	*fast*
return	*almost*	*finish*

Looking up synonyms

Name ______________

Extra special words

✤ Use a thesaurus to help you find as many different words with similar meanings to these four extra special ones.

special

different

difficult

extra

An abc of similarities

✤ With the help of a thesaurus, try to complete this list of words with similar meanings (the words in each group of three begin with the same letter). Don't worry if you can't fill all the spaces!

aghast	amazed	appalled
beat	b ______	b ______
clasp	c ______	c ______
disobey	d ______	d ______
erupt	e ______	e ______
fierce	f ______	f ______
glitter	g ______	g ______
habitation	h ______	h ______
important	i ______	i ______
jolt	j ______	j ______
kin	k ______	k ______
loiter	l ______	l ______
mumble	m ______	m ______
nurse	n ______	n ______
occasion	o ______	o ______
portion	p ______	p ______
quake	qu ______	qu ______
ransack	r ______	r ______
sip	s ______	s ______
taut	t ______	t ______
ugly	u ______	u ______
void	v ______	v ______
wayward	w ______	w ______
yap	y ______	y ______

Name ____________

Finding antonyms

A folding abc of opposites

✤ Use a thesaurus to help you find words which are opposite in meaning to those listed below. They must have the same first letter as the word they disagree with!

argue	agree
bashful	b ____________
careless	c ____________
damp	d ____________
enter	e ____________
fact	f ____________
glee	g ____________
hinder	h ____________
important	i ____________
joyless	j ____________

loathe	l ____________
manage	m ____________
necessary	n ____________
odd	o ____________
permit	p ____________
refined	r ____________
spend	s ____________
thick	t ____________
usual	u ____________
valid	v ____________
worthy	w ____________

Name ________________

What's the difference?

✤ Use a dictionary to help you explain the difference between these homophones – words which sound the same, but are spelled differently.

A hair is ______________

____

but a hare is ______________

____

A place is ______________

____

but a plaice is ______________

____

A sale is ______________

____

but a sail ______________

____

✤ Fill in the labels.

____

____

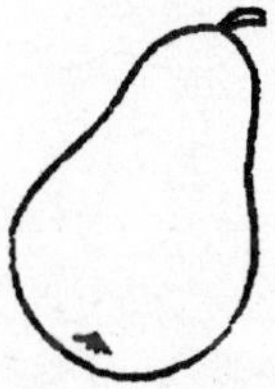

____

cell or sell? ______________

____

____

____

rain or reign? ______________

____

____

____

pair or pear? ______________

____

____

____

Name ____________________

One letter out – what's the difference?

✤ Use a dictionary to help you explain the difference between these pairs of words which have the same sounds but different spellings (by just one letter!).

Cord is ____________________

but a chord ________________

____

A birth is when ____________

____

but a berth ________________

____

A week is _________________

____

but weak means _______

____

✤ Write the correct word on these labels.

____

____

____

A miner is ________________

____

but minor is ______________

____

A ring is __________________

____

but wring means ______

____

We sew __________________

and we sow ______________

__________________________ So!

Name ____________________

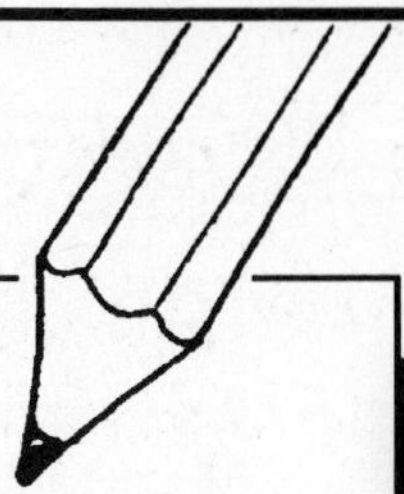

Same words – four different meanings!

✤ With the help of a dictionary show how these words can each have four different meanings.

light

1 ______________________________

____

2 ______________________________

____

3 ______________________________

____

4 ______________________________

____

note

1 ______________________________

2 ______________________________

3 ______________________________

4 ______________________________

match

1 ______________________________

2 ______________________________

3 ______________________________

4 ______________________________

Name ______________

Investigating key story words

The gist of a story

✤ Find a book you like the look of, but do not know.

✤ Read the first few pages, then record the following details.

Title

____

____

by ______________
(author)

Opening few words:

____

Who is it about? (Names of characters mentioned at the beginning.)

____

____

What is it about? (Names of main things and places mentioned at the beginning.)

____

____

____

What happens? (Some of the verbs first used.)

____

____

____

Descriptions (Any adjectives used to describe colour, size, age, character and so on.)

____

____

____

Name ________________

A part-of-speech survey

What kinds of words are used most often?

Most dictionaries tell us what part of speech each listed word is: n. (noun) vb. (verb) adj. (adjective) and so on. Choose any page from your dictionary and rewrite the listed words in these columns (starting at the bottom!) See which column grows tallest!

adj. adjectives	**n.** nouns	**vb.** verbs	**adv.** adverbs	**others,** such as conj. pron. and so on

Name ______________

Investigating most-frequently-used words

A word popularity survey

The ten words given at the bottom of this page are used more often than any others in the English language.

✤ Select a page or two of writing (your own, maybe) and count, by ticking or colouring the boxes below, how many times each of these words appears.

Number of times used										
20										
19										
18										
17										
16										
15										
14										
13										
12										
11										
10										
9										
8										
7										
6										
5										
4										
3										
2										
1										
Words	a	the	to	and	that	in	is	it	of	you

Greetings!

✤ Make a greetings card for a special occasion by cutting out, folding and colouring the part below. Inside write suitable greetings words. (You could use some of those shown on this page.)

Congratulations on your success!
... victory!
... great achievement!

Welcome back!
... home!
... to our school!
... to our club!

Many Happy Returns!
Merry Christmas!
Happy New Year!

Have a wonderful
.... festival!
... birthday!
... celebration!
... holiday!

A very good morning!
... afternoon!
... evening!
Three cheers for friends!

Choosing thank-you words

Name ________________

Writing a thank-you letter

If you had to write a thank-you letter for a present, an invitation, a treat, a stay, or a special kindness, what words would come first to your mind?

✤ Choose and ring ten words from this parcel.

✤ Think of two more suitable words and write them on the top.

✤ Use this guide to help you start your letter. Try to use as many of your chosen words as you can.

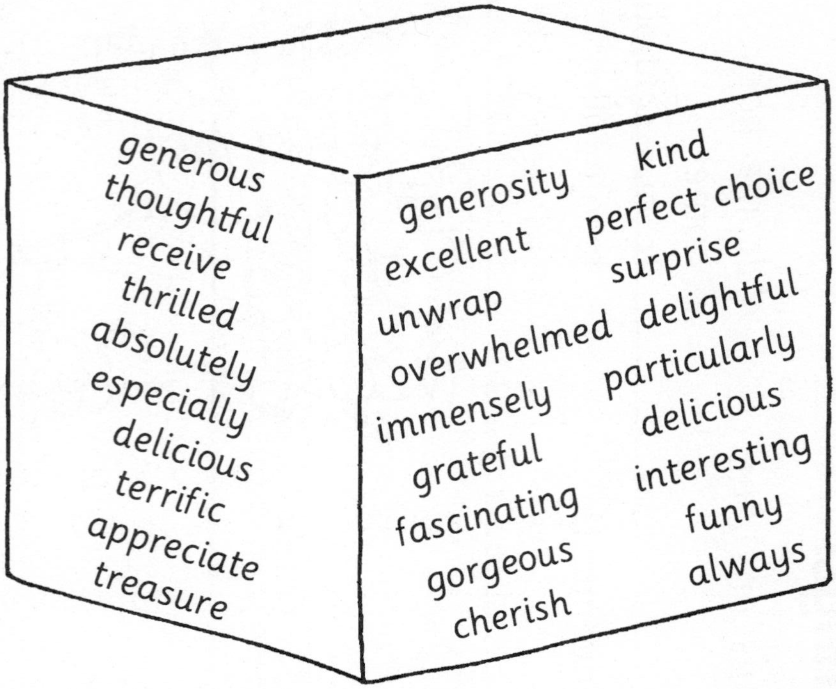

Address: ________________

____

Date: ________________

Dear ________________

Thank you very much for

A request letter

Sometimes we need to write a letter asking for a favour, or information, or because we want to buy something. Here are some words and phrases that you might choose.

✤ Select and underline the ones you want to use. Add your own ideas.

Who? *Dear Sir or Madam (if you do not know the person's name); Mr/Ms ____________ (surname)*

Why? *I have seen your catalogue of / advertisement in*

I'm writing on behalf of ____________ ;

on the recommendation of ____________

Requesting: *Please could you send me ____________ ;*

I would be grateful if you ____________ ;

We wish to ask whether ____________

What? *information; prices; (further) details; free offer; answers to questions*

When? *as soon as possible; by return; within ____________ days; at your convenience*

Enclosures: *I enclose payment; a cheque; a postal order; a stamped addressed envelope*

Conclusion: *With many thanks;*
Yours sincerely;
Yours faithfully

Signature:

Printed name:

✤ Use the words you have chosen to write your own letter.

Name ____________

Questions of spelling: 1

✤ In the sentences below, tick the correctly spelled words and put a cross by the misspelled ones.

1 Is this a house or a horse ?

2 Is this is a mouse or a moose ?

3 Is this a hair or a hare?

4 Wot or what is this?

5 Is it a bird, berd or burd ?

6 Do you ask Weye, Wie or Why?

7 Do you answer because or becoz?

8 Do you write thay , theh or they ?

9 Do you say or sey ?

10 Is it soe , soh , so or soo ?

✤ Check, with a dictionary, any spellings you are still not sure of. Then write the ten correctly spelled words again here.

1 ____________

2 ____________

3 ____________

4 ____________

5 ____________

6 ____________

7 ____________

8 ____________

9 ____________

10 ____________

Questions of spelling 2

✤ In the sentences below, tick the correctly spelled words and put a cross by the misspelled ones.

1 Do you go to school , shcool or skool ?

2 Which looks correct, this riting or this writing ?

3 Is there a problem or is their not a problem?

4 Wehn , when or wen will you ever learn?

5 Do you find this difficult or not at all dificult ?

6 Shhh. Can you be quite or quiet ?

7 Do you like it here or lick it?

8 Do you write sayed , said or sed when you have had something to say?

9 Have you had enough or enuff ?

✤ Check, with a dictionary, any spellings you are still unsure of. Then write the nine correctly-spelled words below.

1 ____________________

2 ____________________

3 ____________________

4 ____________________

5 ____________________

6 ____________________

7 ____________________

8 ____________________

9 ____________________

Name ____________________

Questions of odd spelling

✤ In the passage below, tick the correctly-spelled words and delete the others (with a single line).

What a surprize / cerprise / surprise !
My cister / sister / siister broke my
sissors / scissors / sissers and threw /
threwe / throo them away. I'm surten /
sirtain / certain she did, in fact I'm quite
shor / sure / shore . They are of no more
service / cerviss to me. I wish she would /
wood join a sercuss / sircus / circus. She's
a thurer / thorough newsance/ nuisence/
nuisance , but I still love her reelly / really.

✤ Use a dictionary to check any difficult spellings, then write the twelve correctly-spelled words below.

1 ____________________

2 ____________________

3 ____________________

4 ____________________

5 ____________________

6 ____________________

7 ____________________

8 ____________________

9 ____________________

10 ____________________

11 ____________________

12 ____________________

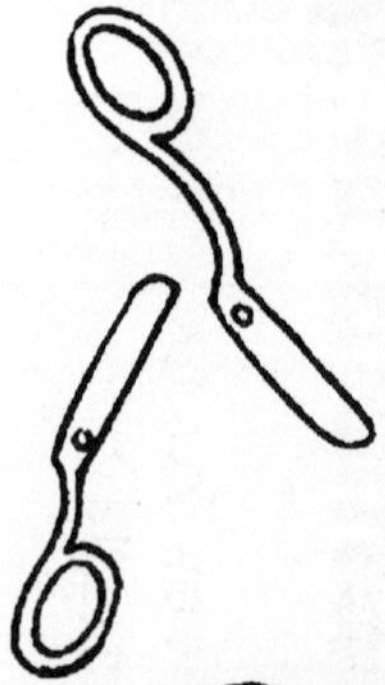

What odd ~~weirds~~! Words

✤ Here are some lines of writing. Find one wrong word in each line, strike it out and rewrite it correctly in the column below.

Let's start with the whether. ____________

Sometimes its just fyne, ____________

sometimes it reigns. ____________

In winter we get called. ____________

In summer we are to hot. ____________

We can never be shore ____________

weather it will be fine ____________

(or knot as the case may be). ____________

Now how about next weak? ____________

Shall we go to the sails? ____________

I need a new pear of shoes, ____________

some wrings for my fingers, ____________

and a big peace of cheese. ____________

I think that will bee all. ____________

Name ____________

Which ~~weird~~ is it?
Word

Here / Hear are some sentences.

✤ Chose / choose the correct spelling and delete the misspelled words.

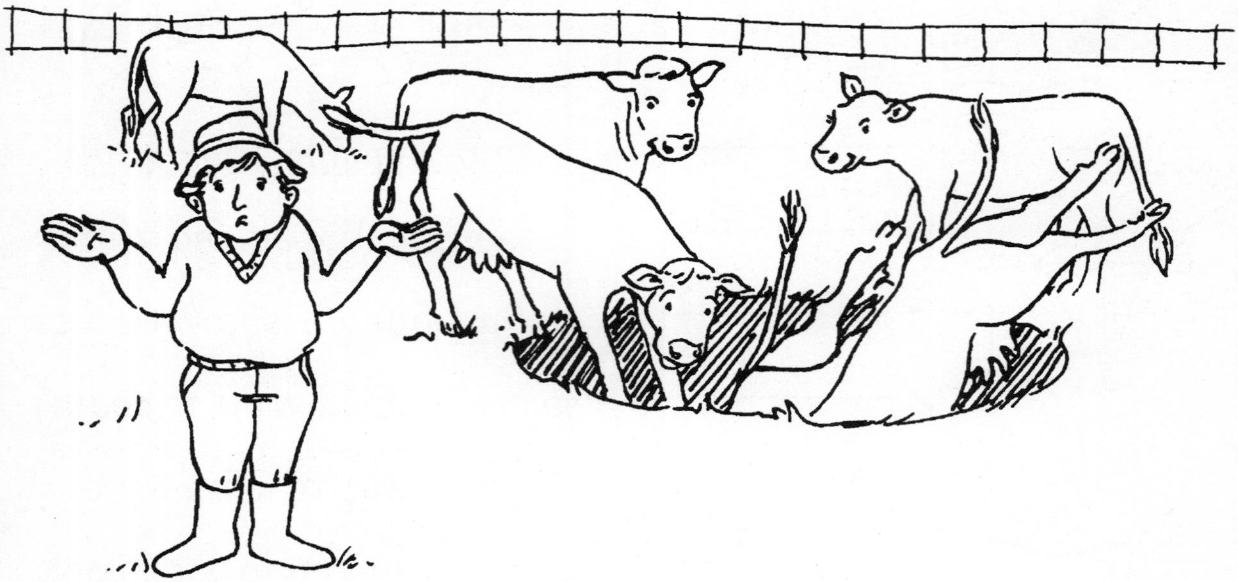

Have you heard / herd about those cows? The whole / hole heard / herd apparently fell into a big whole / hole in the ground.

Never mind / mined!

The new / knew farmer never new / knew. He aught / ought to have none / known but he was a way / away. He refused all together / altogether to accept / except any blame.

Any way / Anyway it's / its quiet / quite quiet / quite now / know.

Can you police / please do a final check / cheque to see if all the weirds / words look good?

Odd ~~weird~~ word out!

This piece of writing contains some words which are wrong.
Next to each wrong word is a number.

✤ Write the words correctly in the numbered spaces below.

It's all about the kind of things we **aught**[1] to do or **aught**[1] not to do. For example, should we be **aloud**[2] to park anywhere we like? Should we be able to **where**[3] anything anywhere, or go **bear**[4] in public? Is it alright to **steel**[5] ? Is it **fayre**[6] to cause **pane**[7] ? Should we all be **maid**[8] to behave much better?

Should we all be free to spell as we wish?

What do you think? ______________________________

____

Do you need to check any words in the dictionary?

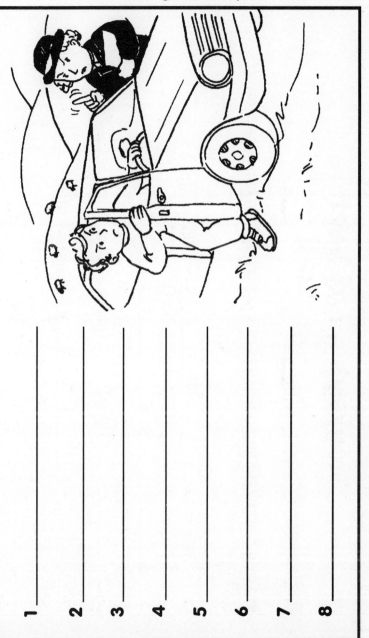

1 ______________

2 ______________

3 ______________

4 ______________

5 ______________

6 ______________

7 ______________

8 ______________

Name ____________

Choosing suitable adjectives and adverbs

Monkey's ..... adventure

This is a very dull story.

✤ Liven it up by adding adjectives and adverbs. Then finish the story in your own way.

Once there was a ____________ monkey. She lived ____________ in a ____________ tree in a ____________ forest. She had ____________ friends. She liked to eat ____________ bananas and ____________ nuts.

One day Monkey decided to have a ____________ adventure. She wanted to find out who else lived in the ____________ forest. So off she went ____________ swinging and ____________ singing. After a ____________ while she met a ____________ elephant. 'Climb on to my ____________ back,' said the elephant. So she did and they charged ____________ through the ____________ trees. But then they met a ____________ tiger.

'Follow me,' said the tiger. So they did, until they met ____________ .

(Continue the story over the page if necessary.)

A 'great' story

✤ Find better, different words to replace the too many 'greats' in this story. Read the whole story before you start writing your words in the spaces.

The sun was shining. It was a great ______________ day. 'Great!' ______________ I thought. I'll go fishing. I got up, had a great ______________ breakfast and then got my stuff together, including my great ______________ new fishing rod. Then I set off on the great ______________ walk to that great ______________ lake. Eventually I got there and found a great ______________ spot for fishing. I cast my line and felt a great ______________ tug. But then I heard 'Snap!' 'Great!' ______________ I hissed, that's all I need, a broken line. It took a great ______________ long time to sort things out, then I started again. I kept thinking of that great ______________ fisherman in the papers, the one who caught a great ______________ pike. Well, in the end I caught three small fish but I had a really great ______________ time anyway.

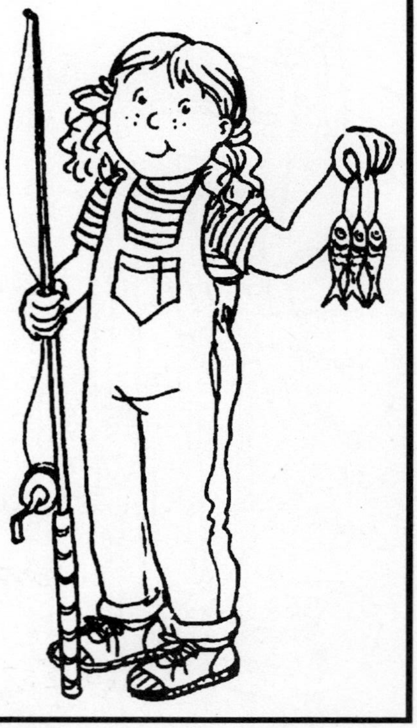

Name ____________

Instead of 'said'

✤ See how many different words you can use instead of 'said' to make this conversation sound more lively. Read the whole discussion before you start choosing your words. Then write them in the spaces provided.

'Hurry up Harry!' said ____________ Dad.

'What are you doing?' said ____________ Dad. 'Hurry up, or you'll be late for school.'

'It's all right Dad,' said ____________ Harry.

'No, it isn't' said ____________ Dad. 'Here's your coat, put it on. We're going now.'

'Can we go by car?' said ____________ Harry.

'No,' said ____________ Dad. 'We're walking.' And so they set off for school.

'Mind that car,' said ____________ Dad. 'Keep on the path.'

'Wait for me!' said ____________ Harry as he lagged behind.

'I'm just going into the shop,' said ____________ Harry.

'Oh no you're not,' said ____________ Dad.

'Look, there's Ben,' said ____________ Harry.

'Hi Ben,' he said ____________ from across the street. They got through the school gate just in time.

'Bye-bye Harry,' said ____________ Dad. The boys went in.

'Good morning,' Miss Jones said ____________ to them.

Going on and on and on

You will need to edit this story.

✤ Break it up into shorter sentences, removing and replacing the word 'and' whenever possible. (Try using while, when, soon, but, because, eventually, afterwards, and so on.) Use a red or blue pen.

On Sunday I went to my nan's ~~and~~ ~~we~~ . We got stuck in a traffic

jam ~~and~~ ~~we~~ . We waited for ages and ages ~~and~~ . When we got

there late ~~and~~ my nan was upset and she thought we

had an accident and we had chicken and chips for dinner

and ice-cream and then we went for a walk in the woods

and I saw a squirrel and I walked up to it and it looked at

me and I put my hand out and then

it ran away up a tree and

we saw some ducks in a pond

and we fed them bits of biscuits

and then it was time to go home.

Name ______________

Is it 'it's' or 'its'?

✤ Choose the right one to fill each space. Remember that 'it's' (with an apostrophe) stands for *it is* while 'its' (without an apostrophe) is to do with belonging.

_______ a beautiful day. The sun is shining in all _______ glory. Just listen to the blackbird singing _______ heart out up on _______ high perch in the park. Down below sits the cat minding _______ own business. _______ just lazing in the sun, licking _______ paws from time to time. For once _______ not raining!

_______ a pity then, that we are stuck indoors. The school – with _______ teachers, _______ children and all _______ other staff – has _______ work to do. _______ a very busy place. School has _______ ups and _______ downs. Never mind, _______ often fun and _______ got _______ pleasures too – like sorting out whether _______ '_______ ' or '_______ '! Or would you rather be in the park with the blackbird singing _______ song?

Name ____________________

My mum

✤ Choose some words for your mum.

My mum is ________________________________

____.

She likes to ________________________________

____.

Sometimes she ________________________________

____.

But always she ________________________________

____.

I ____________________________ my mum.

Is she:
tall,
pretty,
jolly,
kind,
gentle,
busy?

Does she ever:
get cross,
tell tall stories,
play tricks or
sit down?

Does she:
chatter,
laugh,
shout,
sing,
dance or
go shopping?

Has she:
special
friends,
likes,
dislikes,
a twinkle
in her eye?

Name ____________________

Words for a pet

My lovely pet

✤ Draw your own, or imaginary pet, then write about how it looks, feels and behaves.

Does it:	**Is it:**
bark	furry
growl	slimy
purr	warm
wag	gentle
wriggle	fierce
nibble	stripy
gobble	spotty
lick	cuddly
sneeze	cute
snooze	loving
scratch	adorable
swim	tame
creep	terrible
crawl	afraid
or	or
wander?	foolish?

My friend

✤ Use words to create a picture of a special friend. Then draw a portrait.

Favourite words spoken

Appearance
plump? pink-cheeked?

____
____
____
____
____
____

My portrait of:

____

Likes
loud music?
long walks?

____
____
____
____
____
____

Dislikes
washing?
work?

____
____
____
____
____
____

Character
generous? gentle? genius?

____
____
____

Suitable nicknames:

____
____

Typical activities
climbing up walls?
eating ice-cream?

Name ____________

Happy words

✤ Fill this cloud with more words that give you a feeling of happiness.

✤ Why not colour your five happiest words?

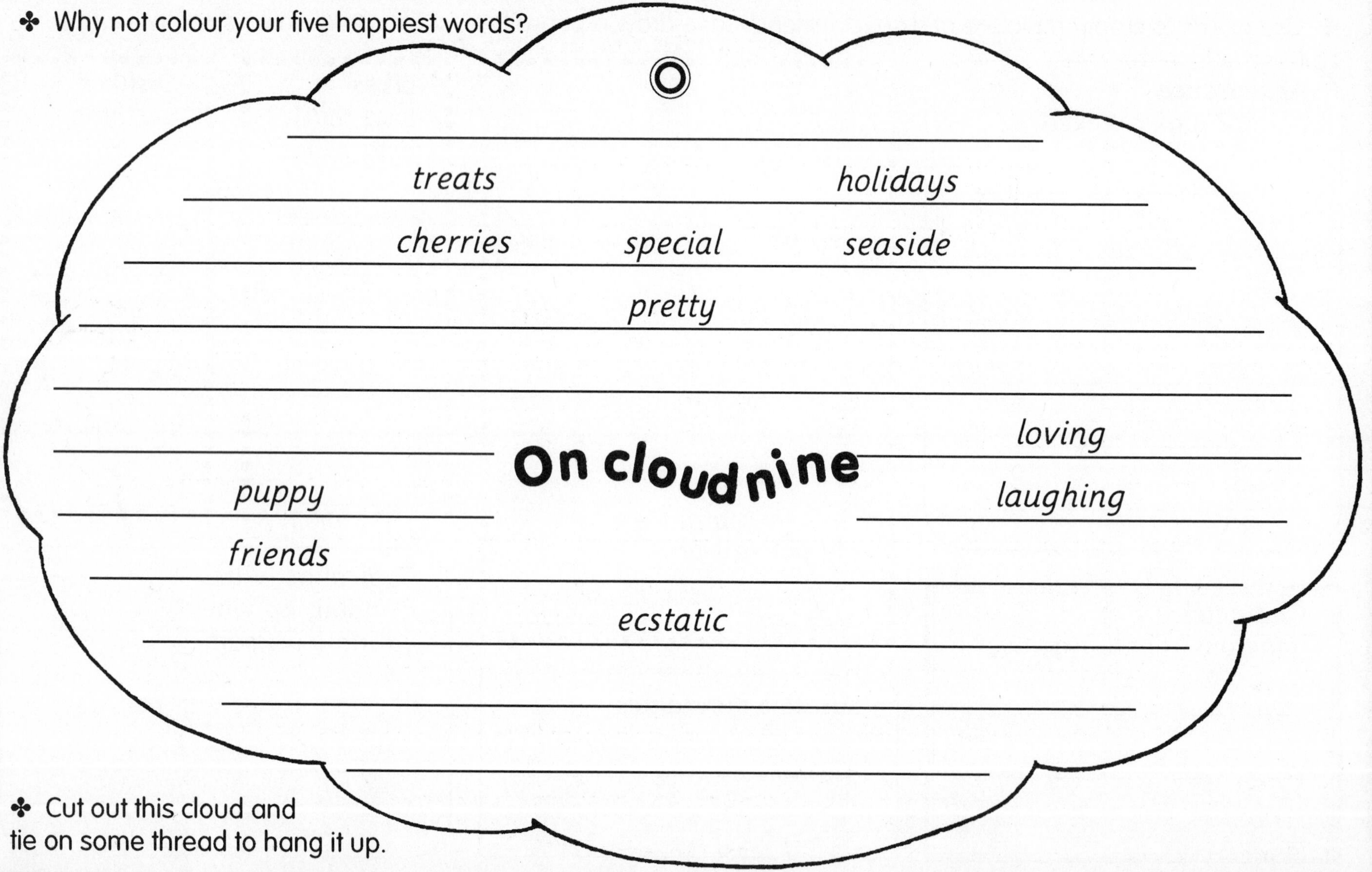

✤ Cut out this cloud and tie on some thread to hang it up.

Name ____________________

Sad words

✤ Can you help fill this face with some more words that make you feel sad?

✤ Colour around some of the words with dismal, dreary colours.

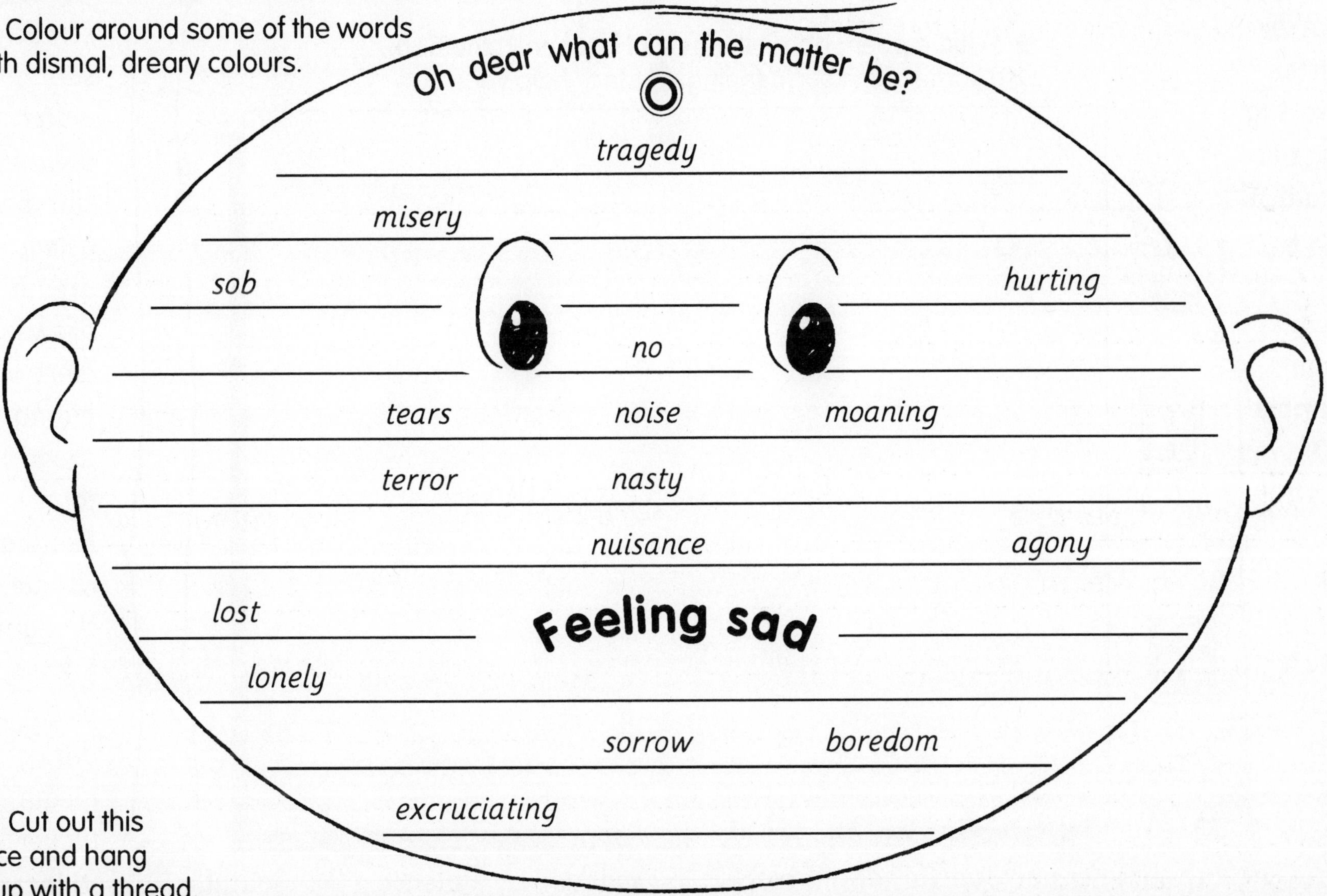

✤ Cut out this face and hang it up with a thread.

Words about darkness

Name ____________________

It was a dark, dark night

✤ Write a poem about things that happen in the dark.
Use some of the surrounding words to help you!

heartbeat
clatter
creaking
scared
afraid
spooky
imagine
rustle
fumble
stumble
sniff
snuffle
stare
trip
stir
mouse
alarm
bark
hoot
howl

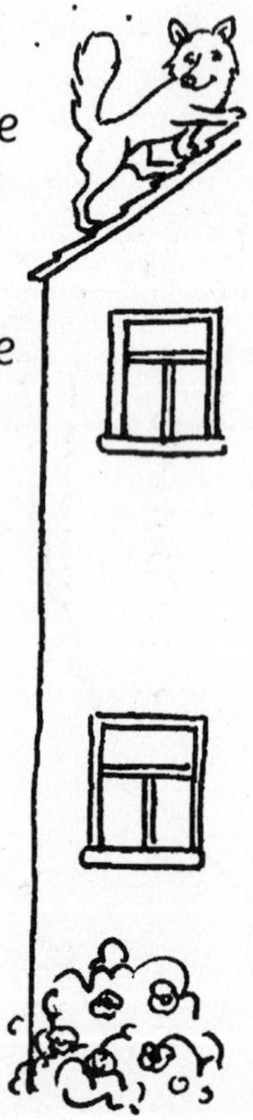

screech
scratch
watch
aware
slumber
asleep
dream
drowsy
alert
hiding
dread
torch
headlight
candle
thoughts
fox
pitch
dark
gleam
flicker

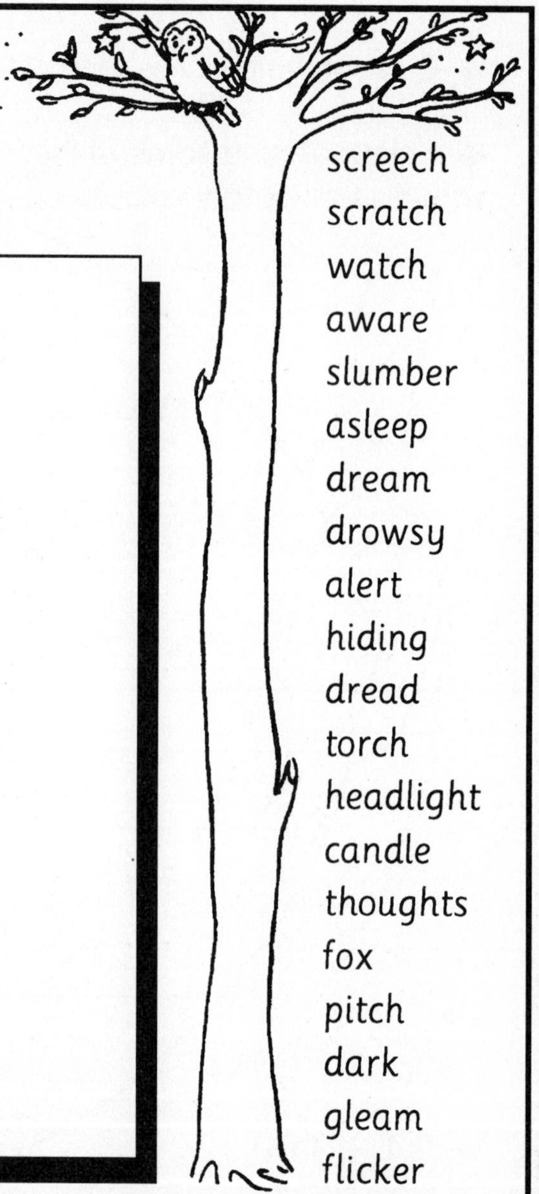

twinkling shimmering nocturnal black sparkle silence solitude stillness

Name ____________________

Fire! Fire!

✤ Write some sentences describing sparks, flames, smoke and ashes to draw a word picture of a whole fire. You can use some of the words around the page to help you.

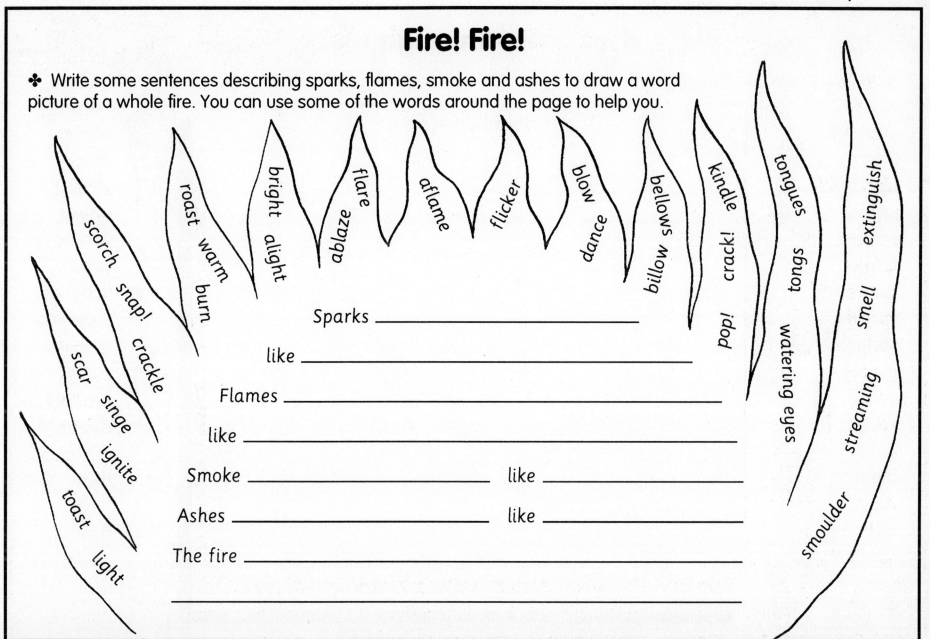

scorch snap! crackle
scar singe ignite
toast light
roast warm burn
bright alight
ablaze flare
aflame
flicker
blow dance
bellows billow
kindle crack! pop!
tongues tongs watering eyes
extinguish smell streaming smoulder

Sparks ____________________

like ____________________

Flames ____________________

like ____________________

Smoke ____________________ like ____________________

Ashes ____________________ like ____________________

The fire ____________________

____

Name ______________

Wet words

Wet through

✤ Write a poem about getting wet in the rain, using some of these words to help you.

drip
drop
plop
pitter
patter
splatter
spitting
spotting
sprinkle
pour
seep
soak
damp
dank
squelch
drench
saturate

Rain, rain, rain, rain

shiver
swim
shower
drown
puddle
splash
beating
battering
trickling
streaming
torrents
downpour
flow
flush
flood
float
sink

Name ____________________

Like a volcano

✤ Write a poem on this volcano describing someone (yourself, maybe) in a rage.
Use some of the erupting words to help you, and continue on extra paper, if you wish.

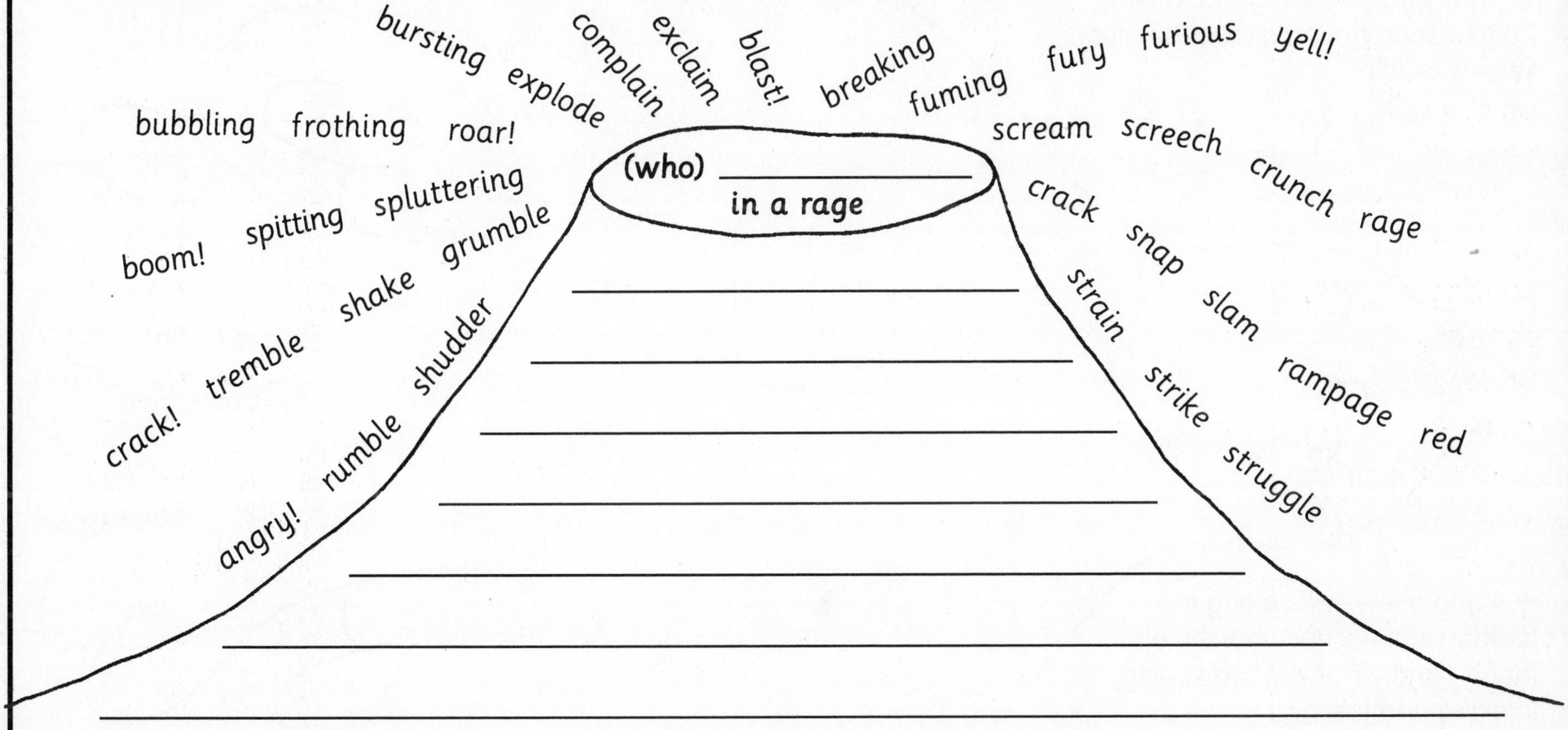

Name ________________

High in the sky words

Like a beautiful bird

✤ Fold this page along the centre fold. Cut out your bird. Fold again, and lift the wings.

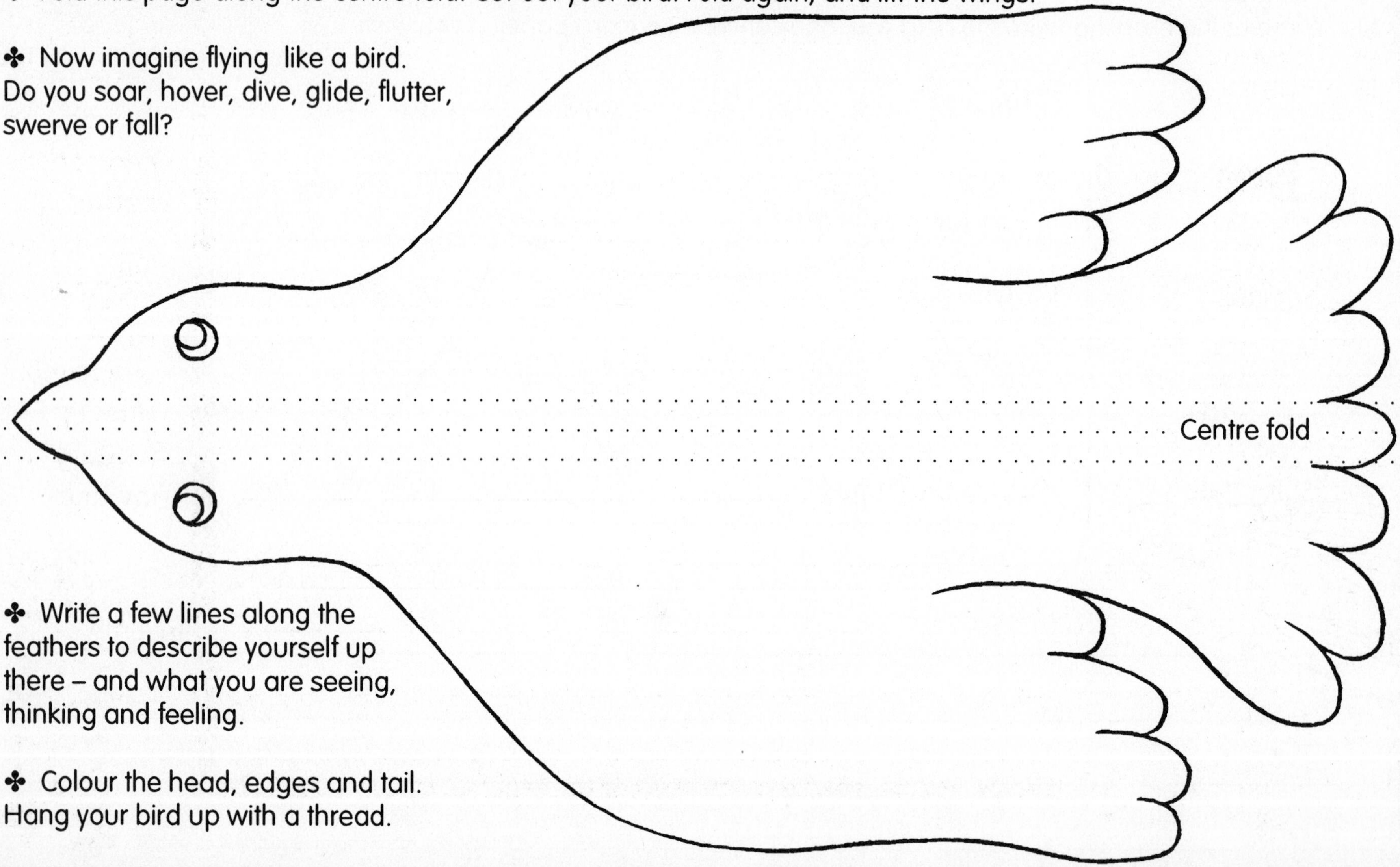

✤ Now imagine flying like a bird. Do you soar, hover, dive, glide, flutter, swerve or fall?

✤ Write a few lines along the feathers to describe yourself up there – and what you are seeing, thinking and feeling.

✤ Colour the head, edges and tail. Hang your bird up with a thread.

Name ____________________

Christmas is coming!

What's happening?

✤ Choose words to fill in the spaces.

Teachers are ______________________________

Grown-ups are ______________________________

____

Children are ______________________________

Streets are ______________________________

Shops are ______________________________

____

Father Christmas is ______________________________

____

Everyone is ______________________________

____

____

busy
busy
busy!
preparations
decorations
parties
pantomimes
crackers
lights
wrapping
singing
exciting
inviting

Name ____________________

On a cold and frosty morning

✤ Find more words to describe what it is like coming to school on a really wintry day!

Wearing ____

____.

Seeing ____

____.

Hearing ____

____.

Feeling ____

____.

Sliding ____

____.

Falling ____

____.

and calling '______________________________'.

Name ____________________

Sing a song of summer days

✤ Fill up this page with a song made of summery words.

Long hot days spent ____________________

____

Rainy days ____________________

____

Days out ____________________

____

Holidays away ____________________

____

Dreamy days ____________________

____

Summer days ____________________

____

Think about

sunshine
picnics
beach
swimming
fairground
sailing
holidays
diving
sand-castles
kites
bikes
wasps
strawberries

Name ______________

Feel good/bad words

Yes to / No to

✤ Describe six things that make you feel good

1

2

3

4

5

6

and six things that you don't like.

1

2

3

4

5

6

Heroes? Particular kinds of foods, behaviour, weather, TV, music or sports? Villains?

Name ____________

What about me?

✤ Name as many parts of this boy's body as you can.

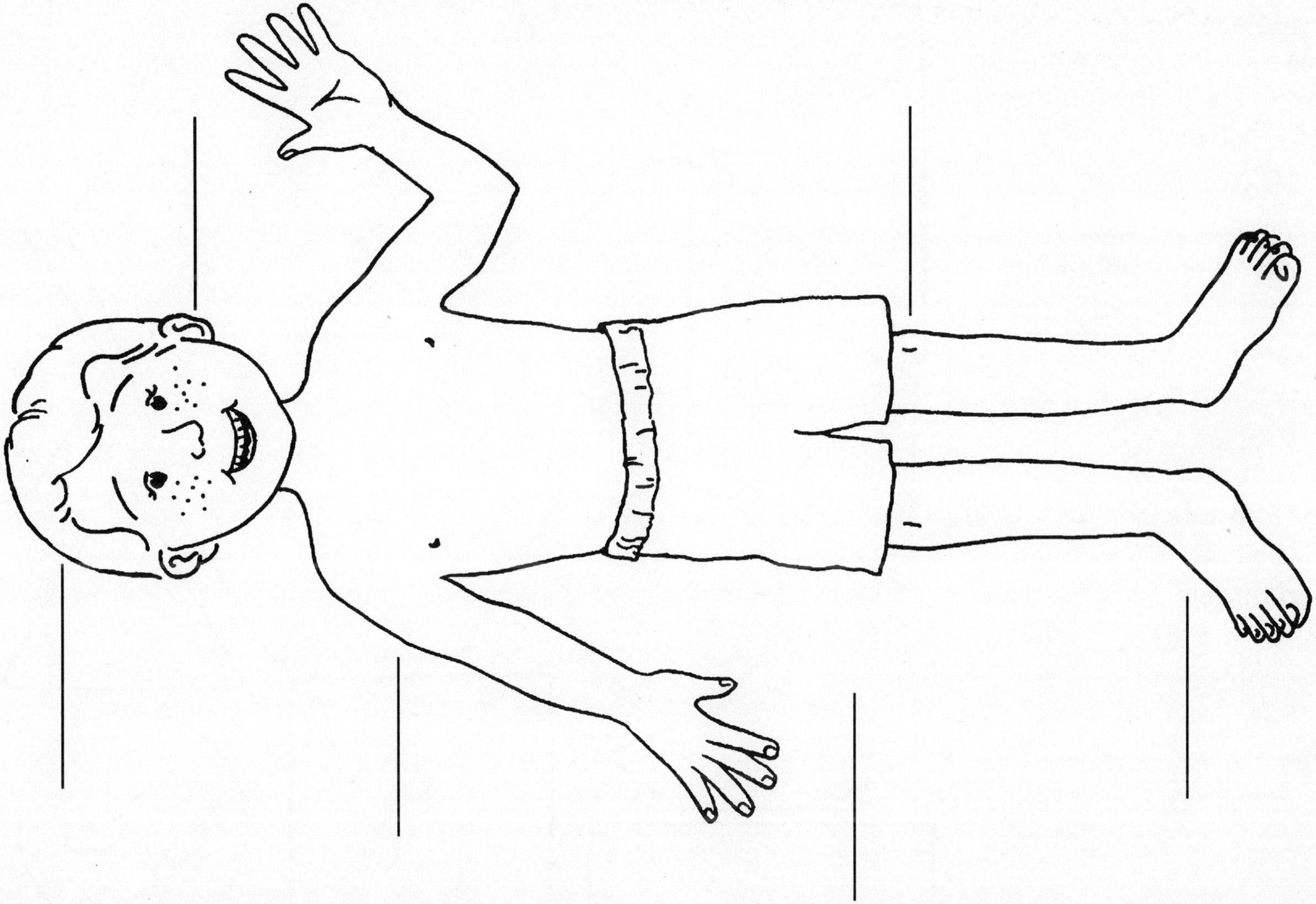

Name ____________

Shape words

Shapes galore

✤ Write the correct name inside each shape in the panel on the right (there are two of each). The table below may help you.

Name of shape	Number of edges/sides
circle	1
semicircle	2
triangle	3
square	4
rectangle (oblong)	4
rhombus (diamond)	4
pentagon	5
hexagon	6

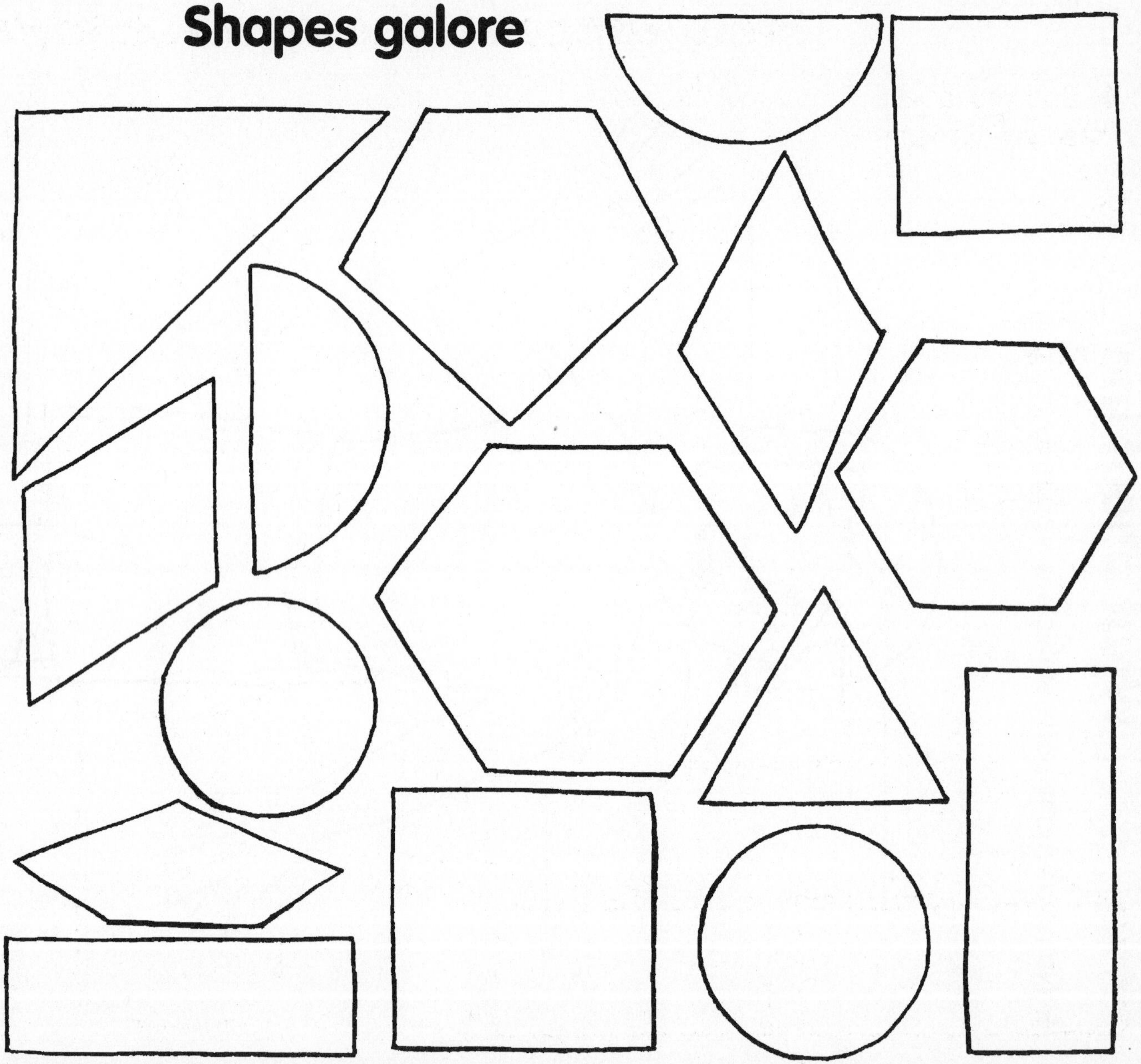

What shapes make up these towers?

✤ Can you label these special shapes?

Clues:

sphere
cube
cuboid
cone
cylinder
tetrahedron

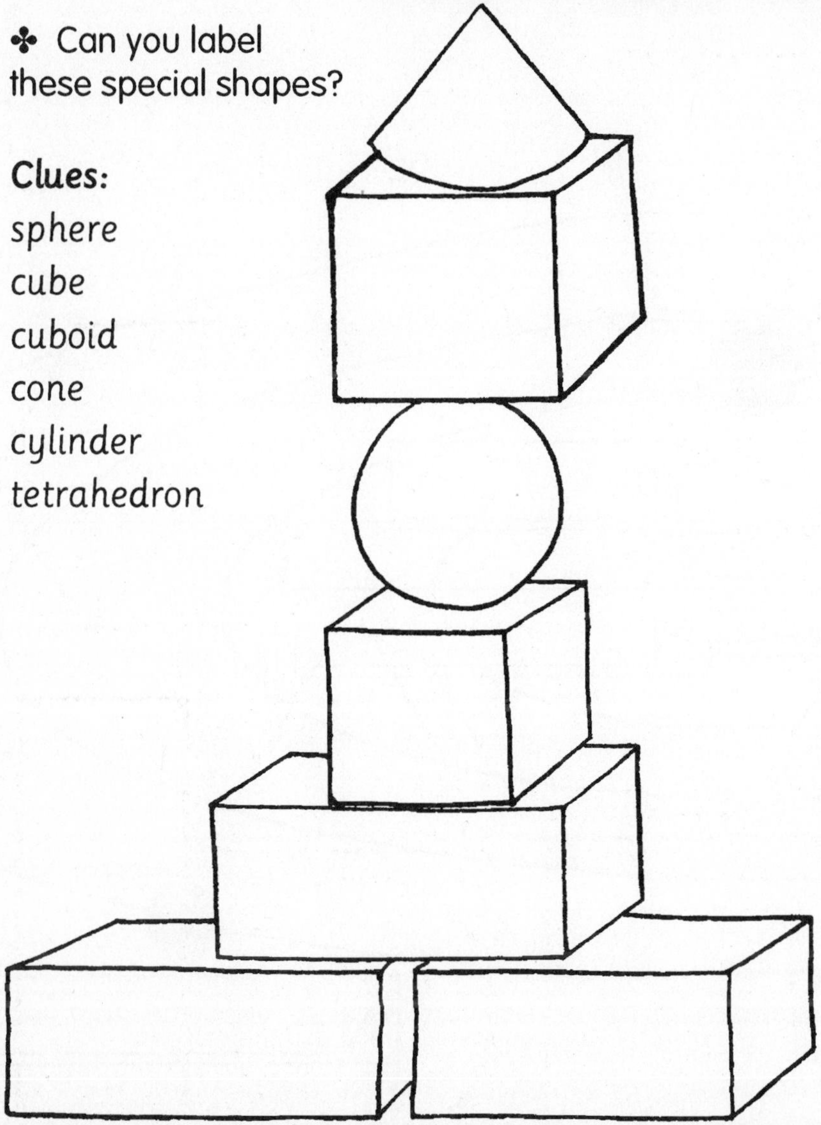

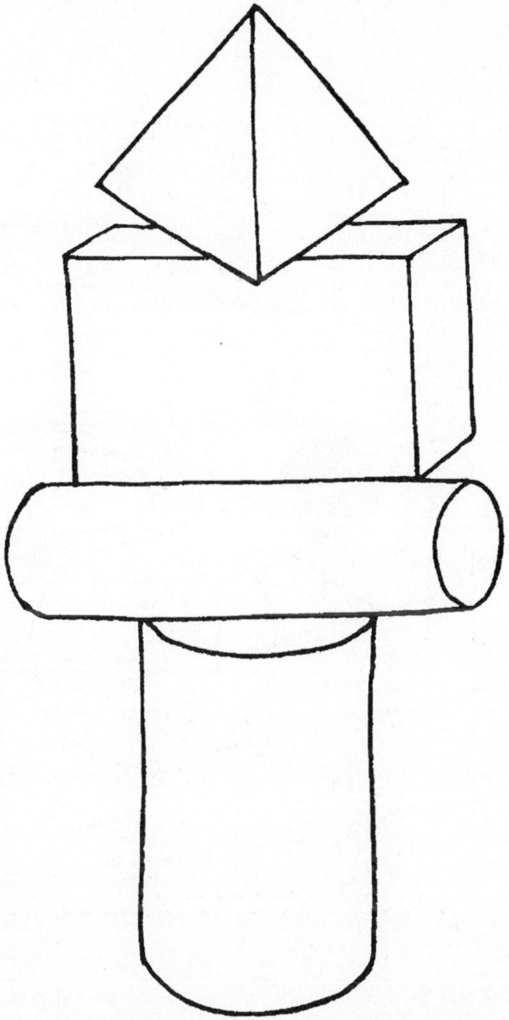

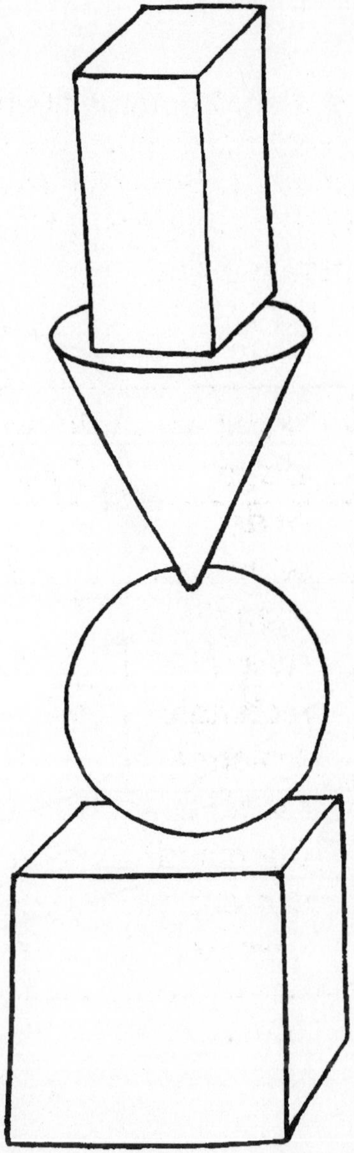

Name ______________

Us (and our neighbours) in space

✤ Can you name the nine planets that orbit the sun?

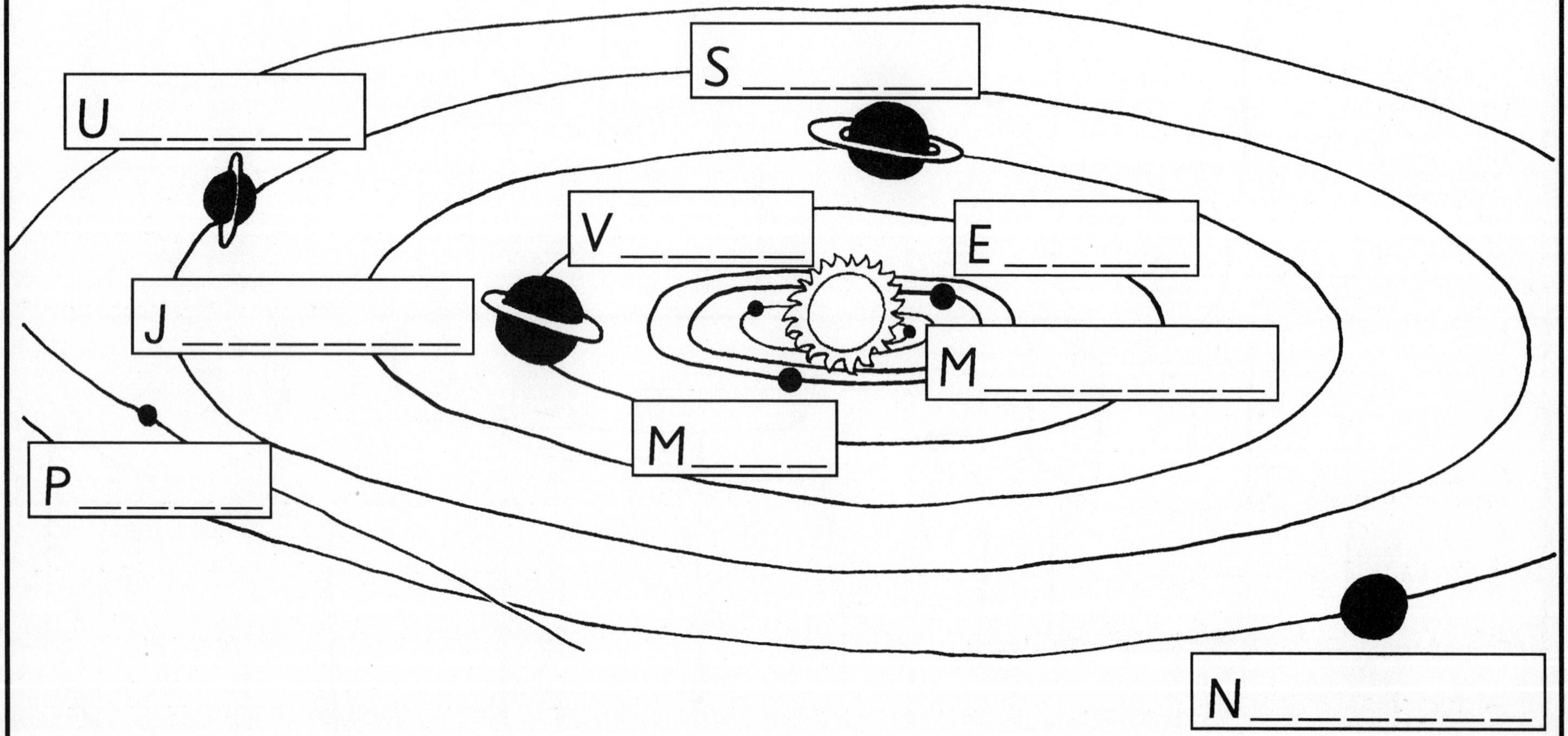

Name ____________________

Times

All these words can be used to express time.

hours years centuries seconds weeks

days and nights months millennia minutes decades

✤ Can you put them in order from shortest to longest on the chart below?

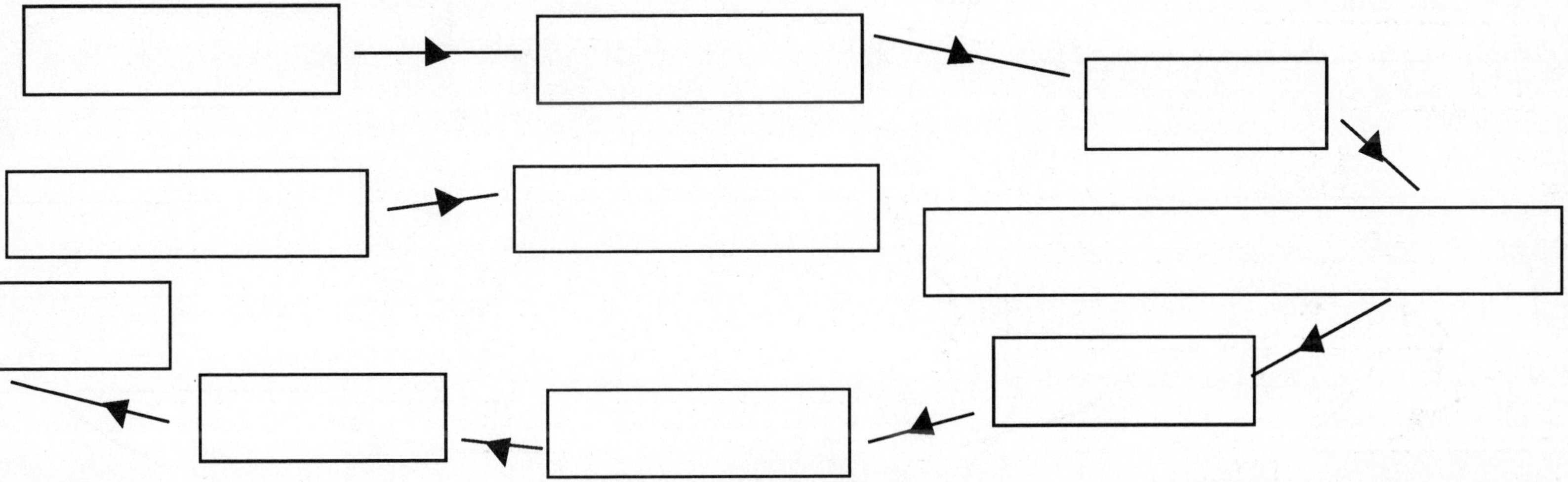

How long are they?

A minute is ____________________

An hour is ____________________

A day and night are ____________________

A week is ____________________

A month is ____________________

A year is ____________________

A decade is ____________________

A century is ____________________

And a millenium is ____________________

Plant words

Name ____________________

Flowers, fruits and vegetables

✤ Can you list the names of flowers, fruits and vegetables that you know?

Flowers

Fruits

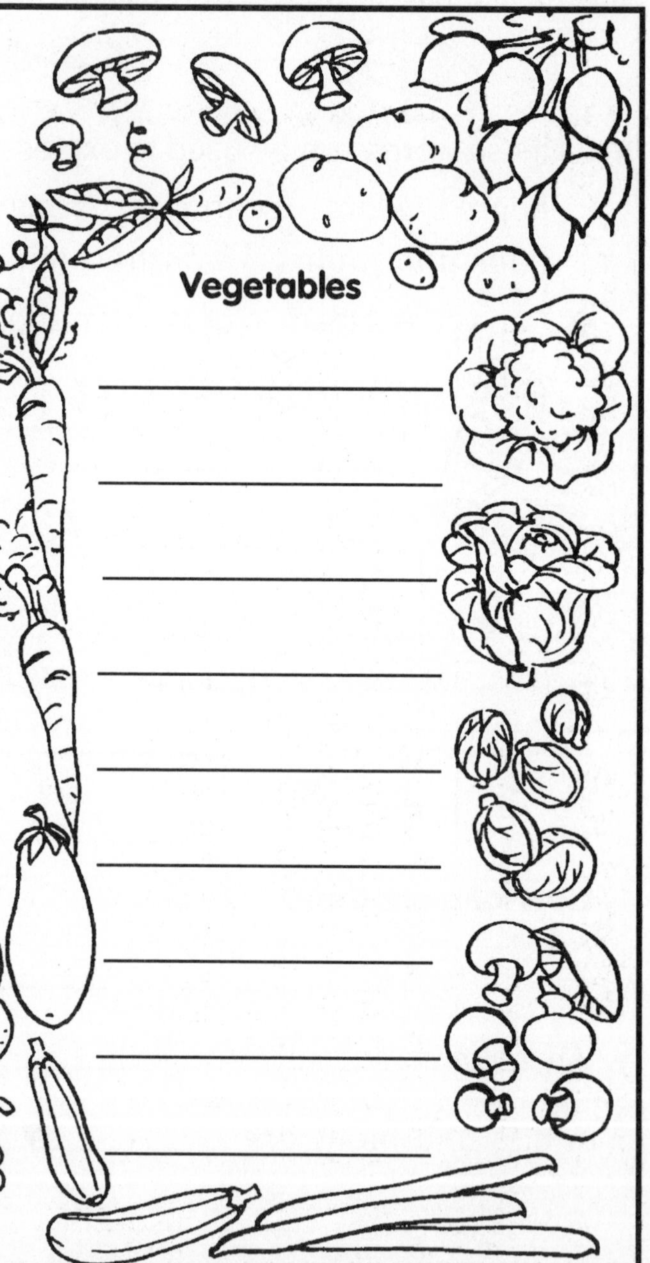

Vegetables

Introduce yourself to insects

Use an information book if you need to.

The main parts of an insect

Most adult insects have three main parts to their bodies – head, thorax and abdomen. They also have antennae (feelers), two eyes, six legs, and most also grow wings.

✤ Can you label the parts here?

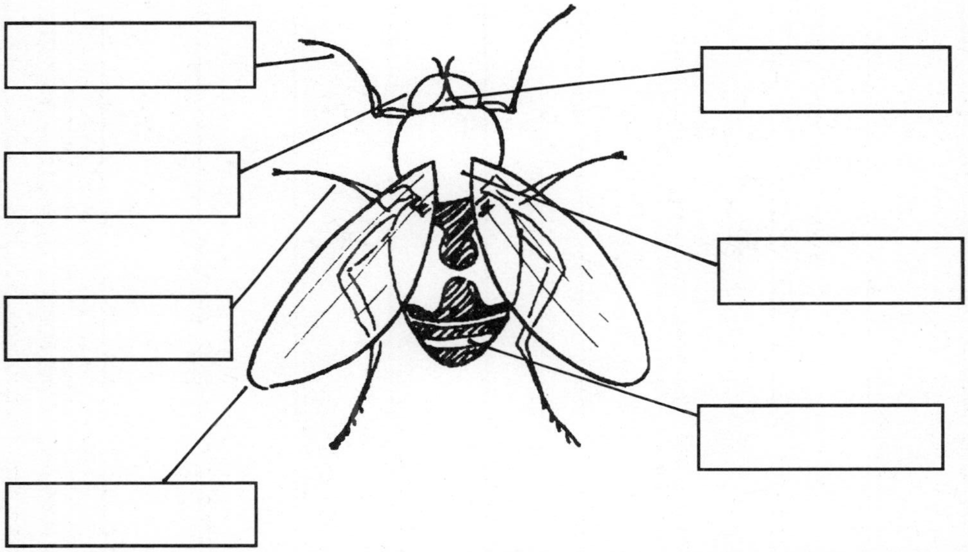

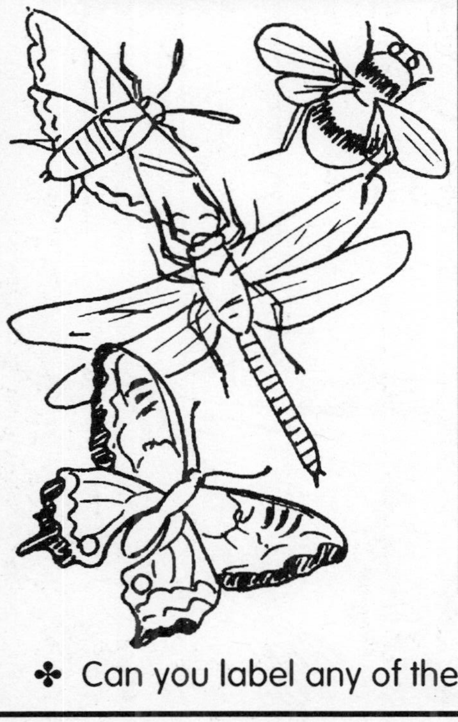

How insects live

Many insects go through four stages in their lives: egg, larva (caterpillar or grub), pupa (chrysalis or cocoon) and adult.

✤ Can you label these stages here?

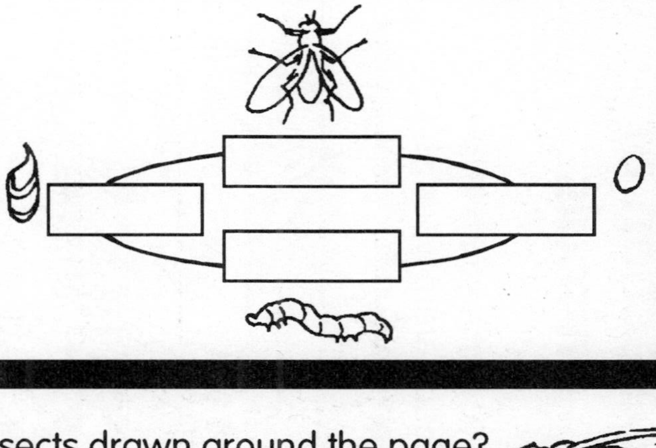

✤ Can you label any of the insects drawn around the page?

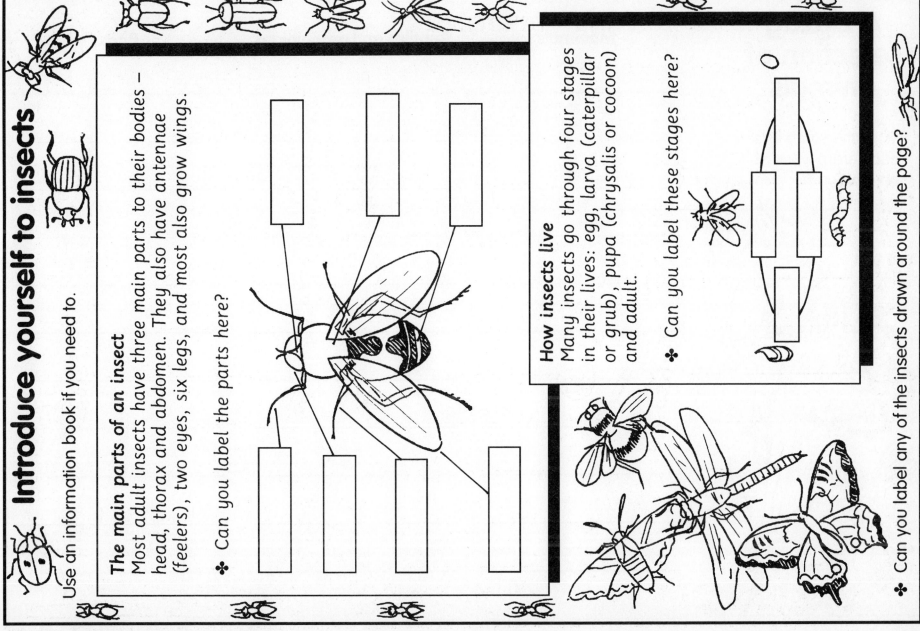

Name ____________

Animal names

A zigzag selection of animals

✤ Make some lists of different types of animals.

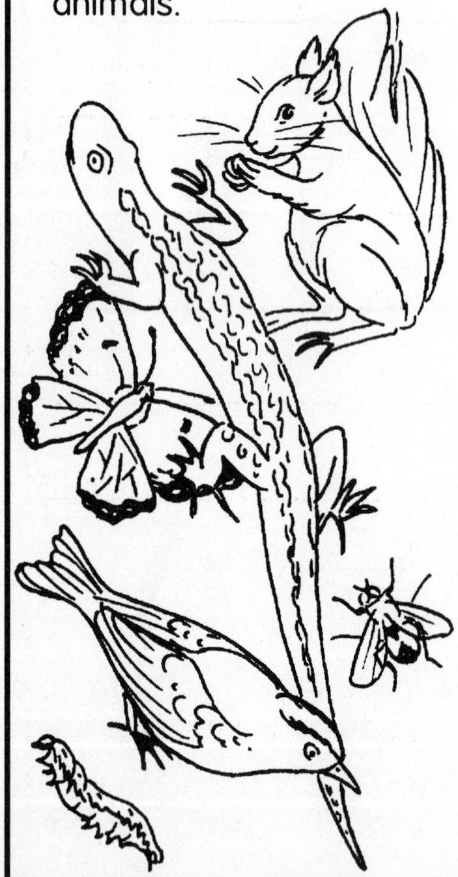

Mammals	Reptiles and amphibians	Birds

A zigzag selection of places

✤ Make lists of towns, counties and countries that you know. Think of places that you've visited, or look at a map or an atlas.

Towns	Counties	Countries
____________	____________	____________
____________	____________	____________
____________	____________	____________
____________	____________	____________
____________	____________	____________
____________	____________	____________
____________	____________	____________
____________	____________	____________

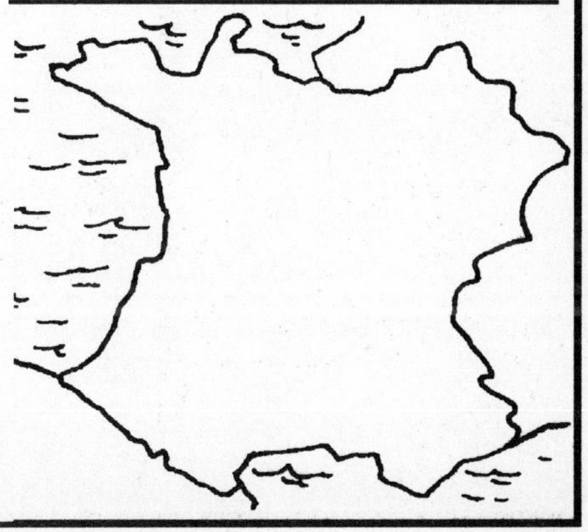

The top ten words

about ____________________
and what they mean

With the help of a good information book, list and explain ten key words of a new subject you are studying.

1. ____________________
2. ____________________
3. ____________________
4. ____________________
5. ____________________
6. ____________________
7. ____________________
8. ____________________
9. ____________________
10. ____________________

Name ____________________

Alliteration – words which begin with the same first letter or first two letters:

____________ ____________ ____________

____________ ____________ ____________

Rhymes – words which end with a similar sound:

____________ ____________ ____________

As it looks **back to front**: ____________________

or **all mixed-up** (an anagram): ____________________

An antonym – a word with opposite or near-opposite meaning: ____________________

I especially like this word because ____________________

____

____

Page 4

My favourite word

A four-page booklet by ____________________

Its dictionary definition: ____________________

____

Synonyms – words of similar meaning

(Thesaurus entries): ____________________

____

The part or parts of speech it plays:

____

____

✤ Use pages 2 and 3 overleaf to write a short story or poem demonstrating the use of your word – and a picture illustrating it.

Page 1

Words in variety

Name ____________

Words you think are **beautiful**

Question words

what? who?

Wonderful words

fabulous gorgeous

Page 4

Amazing words

A four-page booklet by ____________

Noises

atishoo! quack!

Palindromes (words which read the same backwards and forwards)

mum madam

✤ Fill the other side of this page (page 2) with a list of **brief words** – can you find 20 or more two-letter words?

List **long words** on page 3 – can you find 10 or more words with more than 10 letters?

Page 1

Name ______________

Can you find some other words that mean crazy? (Use a thesaurus to help you, if you like.)

mad

Page 4

Crazy Words

A four-page booklet by ______________

Awkward words
Words with odd clusters of consonants like sch wkw tch ght at the beginning, middle or end.

scratch

✣ On pages 2 and 3 on the other side of this sheet make lists of **words with silent letters** (like knight or thumb) and **crazy-looking words** (like biscuit or yacht).

Page 1

Name ______________

New word banking

✤ Collect new words and discover what they mean – try to find one new word each day.

✤ Record each find on a bank ticket, as shown in the example below.

✤ Copy and cut out some more tickets for yourself and store them in a bank book, like the one shown on the following page.

New word: ______________

Meaning: ______________

Date of find: ______________

Place of find: ______________

New word: vocabulary

Meaning: a collection of words

Date of find: ______________

Place of find: ______________

New word: ______________

Meaning: ______________

Date of find: ______________

Place of find: ______________

Name ____________________

Inside back cover

Inside front cover

Words collected

List the words you have collected here:

first fold

Special banking

Assorted vocabulary
collected by

____

back cover

clip

second fold

clip

The official bank book of new words

front cover

Title and contents page

Name ______________________

See my skills with words

extraordinary!

incredible!

By ______________________________

imagination!

expertise!

Contents

1 ______________________________

2 ______________________________

3 ______________________________

4 ______________________________

5 ______________________________

6 ______________________________

7 ______________________________

Continued over the page